D1073364

DIAGNOSTIC & PLACEMENT GUIDE

GLOBE FEARON EDUCATIONAL PUBLISHER
A Division of Simon & Schuster
Upper Saddle River, New Jersey

Printed in the United States of America   4 5 6 7 8 9 10 04 03 02 01

ISBN 0-8359-1592-1

GLOBE FEARON EDUCATIONAL PUBLISHER
A Division of Simon & Schuster
Upper Saddle River, New Jersey

CONTENTS

TO THE TEACHER

Welcome to Globe Fearon's *Access to Math*. This book is the Placement and Diagnosis component. It is designed to help you assess your students' needs as they begin the program and to monitor their progress as they move through the program.

The program itself consists of several individually-bound books, each of which focuses on a specific skill area. This book contains a Locator Test to be administered prior to using the program. The Locator Test will help you to assess students' overall level of achievement in mathematics as well as to pinpoint weaknesses in skill areas. The answer key for this test correlates each test item to the skill area from which it was drawn. This will enable you to determine which books are necessary for each student.

This book also has two parallel tests for each topic taught in the program. Both tests contain the same number of questions and can be used interchangeably. Corresponding questions from Test 1 and Test 2 will correlate with the same lesson in the book and will be of the same level of difficulty. The answer keys for these tests will also indicate the lesson or lessons from which the test item was drawn. You may want to use these tests as pretest and posttest for a given book or to administer alternate versions of a test.

Each of the books in *Access to Math* can be used independently of the other books and there is no defined sequence for the books. You may want to use the results of the Locator Test to help you plan a sequence of topics.

LOCATOR TEST

Solve.

1. 573
    + 459

2. 6,503
    − 3,894

3. 389
    × 437

4. $47\overline{)25{,}004}$

5. $\frac{5}{6} + \frac{3}{4} =$ _____

6. $6\frac{1}{4} - 3\frac{3}{5} =$ _____

7. $2\frac{2}{3} \times 1\frac{3}{8} =$ _____

8. $\frac{2}{5} \div 2\frac{1}{2} =$ _____

9. Charles gets 12 rebounds for every 18 minutes he plays. How many rebounds should Charles get if he plays 24 minutes?   _____

10. At Park, Inc., there are 95 defective parts for every 510 parts manufactured. How many defective parts would there be in 48 manufactured parts?   _____

11. The scale of a blueprint for a house is $\frac{1}{2}$ in. = 3 ft. The width of the living room measures 4 in. on the blueprint. Find the actual width of the living room.   _____

12. The boy is 4 feet tall and casts a 15-foot shadow. The tree casts a 180-foot shadow. What is the height of the tree?   _____

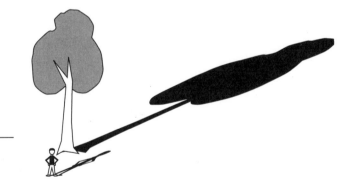

13. Write $6\frac{6}{7}$ as a decimal. Round to the nearest thousandth.   _____

14. 85.11
    − 36.59

15. 45.83
    × 19.7

16. $4.8\overline{)601.92}$

17. What is 84% of 348? Round to the nearest whole number.   _____

18. 60% of what number is 520? Round to the nearest whole number.   _____

19. Wendy wants to buy a coat with a price of $152.75. The coat goes on sale at 15% off. Find the cost of the coat after the discount. Round to the nearest cent.

_____

20. Benito takes out a loan for $575.00. The loan is for 3 years at an interest rate of 7%. Find the amount of interest Benito will have to pay on the loan. Round to the nearest cent.

_____

21. 12 gal = _____ pt

22. 523 g = _____ kg

23. Find the missing side length in the right triangle.

_____

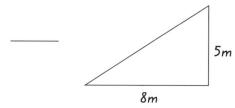

24. Find the area of the circle.

_____

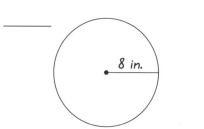

Use the bar graph to solve problems 25–26.

25. How many students are in the class?

_____

26. How many students read above the 8th grade level? Below?

above: _____   below: _____

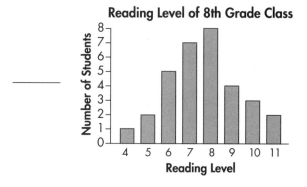

Use the circle graph to solve problem 27.

27. The Viramontes family expenses total $2,480 per month. How much does the family spend on transportation? Round to the nearest cent.

_____

28. Dennis has 56 feet of fencing. Find the area of the largest rectangular region that Dennis can enclose with the fencing.

_____

29. The Venice Manufacturing Company surveyed its 95 employees to find the hours they preferred to work. 24 employees said they liked the night shift. 87 said they liked the day shift. 16 employees liked both the day and night shifts. Find the number of employees that liked *only* the night shift. _____

30. Roberta has to pick up her son from day care at 4:30 pm. She has $1\frac{1}{2}$ hours of shopping to do first. It takes her 20 minutes to get to the day care center. Find the time that Roberta must begin shopping so she can pick up her son on time. _____

31. A rectangle is 12 feet on one side. Its area is 96 square feet. What is the rectangle's perimeter? _____

32. Yvonne worked 8 hours on Monday, 6.5 hours on Tuesday, 4 hours on Wednesday, 7.5 hours on Thursday, and 6.5 hours on Friday. She earns $10.55 per hour. Find Yvonne's earnings for the week. Round to the nearest cent. _____

33. Find the probability of rolling a number that is 4 or greater on a 6-sided cube with faces numbered from 1 to 6. _____

Estimate the answers to problems 34–36.

34. $61.9 \times 8.931 =$ _____

35. $3\frac{1}{3} + 4\frac{6}{7} + 9\frac{4}{5} =$ _____

36. Paul painted 55% of the living room walls. The total area of the walls is 681 square feet. How many square feet has Paul painted? _____

Use the table below to solve problems 37–39.

Florida	Alabama	Georgia	Louisiana	Kentucky	Mississippi	South Carolina	Maryland
6%	4%	4%	4%	6%	7%	5%	5%

37. Find the mean state sales tax. _____ **38.** Find the median state sales tax. _____

39. Find the mode state sales tax. _____

40. Find the probability that tossing a coin 3 times will result in 3 heads. _____

41. Find the probability that a spinner on a wheel with 15 equal areas, numbered 1 through 15, will stop on an odd number. _____

42. A bowl contains 35 numbered balls, 1 through 35. The first ball chosen from the bowl is 32. Find the probability that the next ball chosen will be greater than 29. _____

43. Find the value of n in the formula: $\frac{6n + 12}{2(4+1)} = 6$ _____

44. Find the volume of a cone using the formula volume = $\frac{\pi r^2 h}{3}$, where the radius (r) is 6 cm and the height (h) is 10 cm. Use 3.14 for π. Round to the nearest tenth. _____

45. In the function $5x + 1 = y$, write the ordered pair if $y = 11$. _____

46. Write the prime factorization of 35. _____

47. March 15, 1995, was on a Wednesday. Find the day on which March 15, 2000, will fall. (Hint: 1996 and 2000 are leap years.) _____

48. Write the following number in scientific notation: 5,860,000,000. _____

49. Write the following number in standard notation: 6.4×10^8. _____

50. Simplify the expression $\frac{4^5}{2^5} - (1^2)^4 + (5-1)^3$. _____

TEST 1 WHOLE NUMBERS AND INTEGERS

1. Round 386 to the nearest *ten*. _____

2. Estimate the sum by rounding to the nearest *hundred*.

   539 + 287 = _____

Compute.

3. 74
    501
    +197

4.   356
    − 128

5.   309
    × 438

6. $3^2 \times 3^3 =$ _____

7. Estimate the product by rounding to the nearest *ten*.

   62 × 29 = _____

8. Estimate the quotient by rounding the divisor to the nearest multiple of 10.

   440 ÷ 38 = _____

9. The data processing department of Kim Financial Services went to lunch. The total bill is $168. If there are 14 people and they decide to split the bill evenly, how much does each person owe?   _____

10. Jose went shopping for clothes. He bought a shirt for $12, pants for $23, and a belt for $8. How much change did Jose have left if he gave the cashier $60?   _____

11. Use the < or > symbol to compare these numbers.

    $^-8$ _____ $^+3$

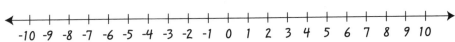

12. Add these numbers using the number line above.

    $^-5 + 6 + {}^-3 =$ _____

Compute.

13. $^{+}8 + {}^{-}5 + {}^{-}1 + {}^{-}7 + {}^{+}4 =$ _____

14. $^{-}180 + {}^{+}75 + {}^{-}13 + {}^{+}41 =$ _____

15. $^{-}4 - {}^{-}5 - 8 =$ _____

16. $297 - {}^{-}42 - 35 =$ _____

17. $^{+}18 - {}^{-}43 + {}^{-}165 =$ _____

18. $^{-}31 \times {}^{-}26 =$ _____

19. $2^2 - ({}^{-}576 \div 24) - 6 =$ _____

20. $(3 \times 2) + 16 + 34 \div 2 =$ _____

21. $52 \times (17 - 12) =$ _____

22. Larry works in the graphics department of his company. A shipment of colored pens arrived recently. There were 45 blue pens that were divided among 15 employees. The shipment contained twice as many red pens, which were divided among 6 employees. If Larry got a share of both colored pens, how many pens did he get? _____

23. $\left| {}^{+}39 \right| - \left| {}^{-}18 \right| =$ _____

Use the coordinate grid to answer questions 24–25.

24. Which point has coordinates $(2, {}^{-}5)$? _____

25. What are the coordinates of point A? _____

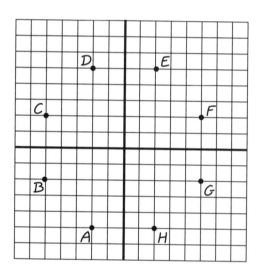

TEST 2 WHOLE NUMBERS AND INTEGERS

1. Round 274 to the nearest *hundred*._____

2. Estimate the sum by rounding to the nearest *ten*.

   419 + 281 = _____

Compute.

3.   84
      260
    +239

4.   308
    − 244

5.   384
    × 207

6. $4^3 + 4^2 =$ _____

7. Estimate the product by rounding to the nearest ten.

   48 × 21 = _____

8. Estimate the quotient by rounding the divisor to the nearest multiple of 10.

   180 ÷ 32 = _____

9. Carlsbad Construction Company received a $1,680 bonus for completing a project ahead of schedule. If the bonus is divided evenly among the 14 workers, how much will each worker receive?   _____

10. Soo Jung bought a box of candy containing 36 pieces of chocolate. She ate 4 of the pieces. She decided to split the rest evenly among her 4 sisters. How many pieces of chocolate should Soo Jung give each sister?   _____

11. Use the < or > symbol to compare these numbers.

    $^+6$ _____ $^-4$

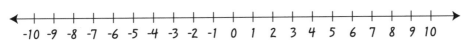

12. Add these numbers on the number line above.

    9 + $^-$6 + 4 = _____

Compute.

13. $^-1 + {}^+3 + {}^-8 + {}^+2 + {}^-3 =$ _____

14. $^-18 + {}^+123 + {}^-89 + {}^-37 =$ _____

15. $9 - {}^-5 - {}^-8 =$ _____

16. $^-32 - 176 - {}^-55 =$ _____

17. $^-149 + {}^-192 - {}^-35 =$ _____

18. $9 + 51 \times {}^-12 =$ _____

19. $3^2 + (6 - {}^-512) \div {}^-2 =$ _____

20. $4^2 \times 3 + 67 - 30 \div 6 =$ _____

21. $112 \div (13+1) - (6 - {}^-5) =$ _____

22. Elizabeth went out to dinner 2 times during the month. She split the bill evenly with her companions each time. The first dinner cost $36 dollars with 3 people eating. The second dinner cost twice as much with 8 people eating. How much did Elizabeth spend for the 2 dinners? _____

23. $\left| {}^-8 \right| + \left| {}^-23 \right| =$ _____

Use the coordinate grid to answer questions 24–25.

24. Which point has coordinates of $(^-3, 4)$? _____

25. What are the coordinates of point E? _____

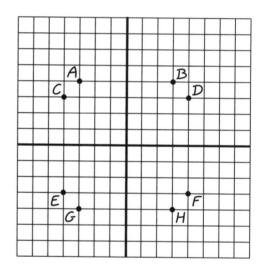

TEST 1 FRACTIONS

1. Find the prime factors of 30. _____

2. Find the least common multiple of 5 and 3. _____

3. Carlos wrote 4 of the 7 reports he has to complete this week. What fraction of the reports has he finished? _____

4. Rename the fraction $\frac{8}{12}$ in simplest form. _____

5. Rename the following fractions so they have the LCD as their denominator.

   $\frac{1}{4}$ _____ $\frac{5}{6}$ _____

6. Rename the fraction $\frac{3}{4}$ as a decimal. _____

7. Rename .55 as a fraction in simplest form. _____

8. Order the following fractions from *least* to *greatest*.

   $\frac{2}{5}$ $\frac{2}{3}$ $\frac{3}{8}$ _____ , _____ , _____

9. Express the following improper fraction as a mixed number.

   $\frac{25}{8}$ _____

10. Express the following mixed number as an improper fraction.

    $5\frac{2}{3}$ _____

11. Express the following decimal number as a mixed number in simplest form.

    3.25 _____

12. Estimate the sum.

    $7\frac{3}{5} + 6\frac{1}{10}$ _____

13. Add. Write the answer in simplest form.

    $\frac{4}{9} + \frac{7}{9}$ _____

14. Add. Write the answer in simplest form.

$\frac{3}{4} + \frac{2}{3}$ _____

15. Add. Write the answer in simplest form.

$4\frac{3}{8} + 3\frac{5}{6}$ _____

16. Subtract. Write the answer in simplest form.

$\frac{11}{12} - \frac{5}{12}$ _____

17. Subtract. Write the answer in simplest form.

$\frac{3}{4} - \frac{2}{3}$ _____

18. Hamid needs to cut $1\frac{3}{8}$ in. from a pipe measuring $3\frac{9}{16}$ in. How much of the pipe will be left? _____

19. Blake needs $4\frac{1}{2}$ cups of flour to bake bread for a Thanksgiving dinner. He has only $1\frac{3}{4}$ cups of flour. How much more flour does Blake need? _____

20. Multiply. Write the answer in simplest form.

$\frac{4}{5} \times \frac{2}{3} =$ _____

21. Multiply. Write the answer in simplest form.

$3\frac{1}{5} \times 2\frac{1}{7}$ _____

22. Divide. Write the answer in simplest form.

$\frac{4}{5} \div \frac{1}{2}$ _____

23. Marina has $3\frac{1}{2}$ pounds of applesauce to divide into $\frac{1}{4}$-pound servings. How many servings will she have? _____

24. 24 of the 28 children in Ms. Sanchez's first grade class are present. What percent of the children are present? (Round to the nearest whole percent.) _____

25. One serving of Luke's favorite ice cream contains 15% of the daily requirement for calcium. What fraction of his calcium needs are in Luke's ice cream? _____

TEST 2 FRACTIONS

1. Find the prime factors of 35. _____

2. Find the least common multiple of 5 and 6. _____

3. Maria spent 3 hours of her 8-hour workday in meetings. What fraction of the day did she spend in meetings? _____

4. Rename the fraction $\frac{9}{12}$ in simplest form. _____

5. Rename the following fractions so they have the LCD as their denominator.

   $\frac{1}{6}$ _____ $\frac{4}{9}$ _____

6. Rename the fraction $\frac{3}{8}$ as a decimal. _____

7. Rename .875 as a fraction in simplest form. _____

8. Order the following fractions from *least* to *greatest*.

   $\frac{1}{3}$ $\frac{3}{8}$ $\frac{2}{7}$ _____, _____, _____

9. Express the following improper fraction as a mixed number.

   $\frac{13}{3}$ _____

10. Express the following mixed number as an improper fraction.

    $4\frac{3}{7}$ _____

11. Express the following decimal as a mixed number in simplest form.

    5.2 _____

12. Estimate the difference.

    $6\frac{4}{9} - 5\frac{7}{8}$ _____

13. Add. Write the answer in simplest form.

    $\frac{5}{7} + \frac{6}{7}$ _____

14. Add. Write the answer in simplest form.

$\frac{1}{4} + \frac{5}{6}$ _____

15. Add. Write the answer in simplest form.

$2\frac{5}{8} + 6\frac{2}{3}$ _____

16. Subtract. Write the answer in simplest form.

$\frac{7}{9} - \frac{4}{9}$ _____

17. Subtract. Write the answer in simplest form.

$\frac{4}{5} - \frac{2}{3}$ _____

18. Huong's house is $4\frac{1}{2}$ mi from his office. On his way to work, he stops for gas after driving $2\frac{2}{5}$ mi. How much farther does Huong have to drive to reach his office? _____

19. Christina is packing a carton that can hold up to $8\frac{1}{4}$ pounds. She has put $4\frac{1}{2}$ pounds into the carton already. How many more pounds can she pack into the carton? _____

20. Multiply. Write the answer in simplest form.

$\frac{3}{4} \times \frac{2}{3}$ _____

21. Multiply. Write the answer in simplest form.

$3\frac{1}{3} \times 1\frac{4}{5}$ _____

22. Divide. Write the answer in simplest form.

$\frac{2}{3} \div \frac{3}{8}$ _____

23. Tasheena needs to cut a $5\frac{1}{2}$-foot board into $\frac{3}{4}$-foot pieces. How many pieces will Tasheena have? _____

24. Nicholas ate a breakfast of 500 calories. He is on a 2,400 calorie per day diet. What percent of his daily calories did Nicholas consume for his breakfast? (Round to the nearest whole percent.) _____

25. In the mayoral election, Janice Kim received 44% of the vote. What fraction of the vote did she get? _____

RATIOS AND PROPORTIONS

1. Write the following ratio in two ways:

   3 blue to 7 orange   _____, _____

2. Are the following ratios equivalent? $\dfrac{10}{12}$ $\dfrac{15}{18}$ _____

3. Write the ratio as a fraction in simplest form: 10 oz to 1 lb 6 oz   _____

4. Write the decimal as a ratio in simplest form: .375   _____

5. Compare the ratios. Use < or >.   8:5 _____ 7:4

6. Order the ratios from least to greatest: $\dfrac{7}{10}, \dfrac{5}{8}, \dfrac{13}{20}$ _____, _____, _____

7. Find the unit rate: $74.08 for 8 hours _____

8. Find the unit cost: 8 lb of chicken for $5.92 _____

9. Pete gives up an average of four walks for every 9 innings he pitches. If he continues at the same ratio, how many walks will he give up after pitching 108 innings?   _____

10. Do the ratios form a proportion? $\dfrac{8}{14}$ $\dfrac{12}{21}$ _____

11. Do the ratios form a proportion? $\dfrac{4}{5}$ $\dfrac{60}{80}$ _____

12. Solve using number sense. $\dfrac{2}{9} = \dfrac{x}{27}$ _____

13. Eduardo's laser printer produces 8 pages every minute. How many pages can Eduardo print in 1 hour?   _____

14. Write a proportion to solve. 10 calculators for $2.30; 32 calculators for $x.   _____

15. Mahmoud ran a 2-mile race in 9 minutes. What speed did he run the race in feet per second? Round to the nearest hundredth. (Hint: 1 mi = 5,280 ft)   _____

16. If the length of the kitchen measures 2.5 inches in the drawing, what is the actual length of the room?

_____

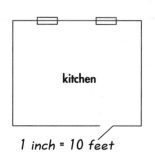

kitchen

1 inch = 10 feet

17. If the distance between the office and school measures $\frac{3}{4}$ inch on the map, what is the actual distance in miles?

_____

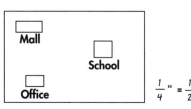

Mall

School

Office

$\frac{1}{4}$" = $\frac{1}{2}$ mile

18. A and B are similar triangles. What is the length of the missing side of triangle B?

_____

19. What is the length of the missing side of triangle A?

_____

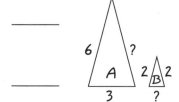

6   ?

A

3

2 2
B
?

20. If the shadow cast by the yardstick is 6 feet and the shadow cast by the side of the house is 54 feet, what is the height of the house in feet?

_____

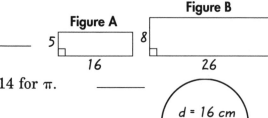

1 yd = 3 ft   6'   54'

21. Are figures A and B similar quadrilaterals?

_____

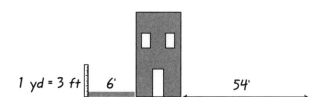

Figure B

Figure A

5   8

16   26

22. Find the circumference of the circle. Use 3.14 for π.

_____

23. Compute the area of a circle with a radius of 4 mm. Express your answer using π.

_____

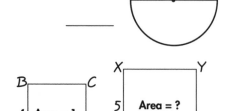

d = 16 cm

24. For the pair of squares, find the ratio of the side lengths. Use it to find the missing area.

$\frac{AB}{WX}$ = _____ ; $\frac{\text{area of ABCD}}{\text{area of WXYZ}}$ = _____

Area of WXYZ = _____

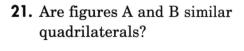

B   C   X   Y

1   Area = 1   5   Area = ?

A   1   D   W   5   Z

25. Find the volume of the cube.

_____

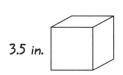

3.5 in.

RATIOS AND PROPORTIONS

1. Write the following ratio in two ways: 6 apples for 5 people. _____ , _____

2. Are the following ratios equivalent? $\dfrac{12}{14}$ $\dfrac{18}{21}$ _____

3. Write the ratio as a fraction in simplest form: 7 nickels to 5 dimes _____

4. Write the decimal as a ratio in simplest form: 0.45 _____

5. Compare the ratios. Use < or >. 5 to 9 _____ 17 to 30

6. Order the ratios from least to greatest: $\dfrac{3}{5}, \dfrac{4}{7}, \dfrac{15}{28}$ _____ , _____ , _____

7. Find the unit rate: 75 miles in 2.5 hours _____

8. Find the unit cost: $24.30 for 18 gal of gas _____

9. If Jamal hits home runs at a ratio of 1 for every 18 at-bats, how many home runs will he have hit after 234 at-bats? _____

10. Do the ratios form a proportion? $\dfrac{9}{15}$ $\dfrac{12}{21}$ _____

11. Do the ratios form a proportion? $\dfrac{4}{5}$ $\dfrac{80}{100}$ _____

12. Solve using number sense. $\dfrac{3}{5} = \dfrac{x}{25}$ _____

13. Jung can assemble 3 circuit boards in 20 minutes. How many circuit boards can he assemble in 3 hours? _____

14. Write a proportion to solve. $87.50 to change 4 tires; x to change 6 tires. _____

15. Rocio walks at a rate of 4 miles per hour. What is her walking rate in feet per minute? (Hint: 1 mi = 5,280 ft) _____

16. If the distance between the doors is 3 inches in the drawing, what is the length of the family room? _____

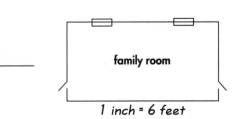

1 inch = 6 feet

17. If the distance between La Costa and Brighton measures $\frac{3}{4}$ inch on the map, what is the actual distance between the two cities? _____

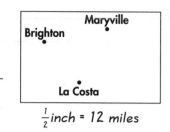

$\frac{1}{2}$inch = 12 miles

18. A and B are similar triangles. What is the length of the missing side of triangle B? _____

19. What is the length of the missing side of triangle A? _____

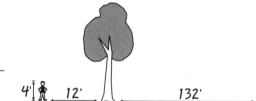

20. The boy is 4 feet tall and casts a 12-foot shadow. The tree casts a 132-foot shadow. What is the height of the tree? _____

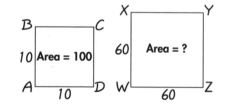

$4'$ $12'$ $132'$

21. Are figures A and B similar quadrilaterals? _____

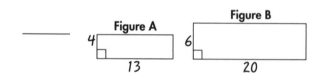

Figure A

Figure B

4 13 6 20

22. Find the circumference of the circle. Use 3.14 for π. _____

23. Compute the area of a circle with a radius of 5 in. Express your answer using π. _____

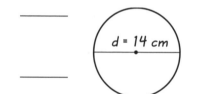

d = 14 cm

24. For the pair of squares, find the ratio of the side lengths. Use it to find the missing area.

$\dfrac{AB}{WX} =$ _____ ; $\dfrac{\text{area of ABCD}}{\text{area of WXYZ}} =$ _____

Area of WXYZ = _____

B C X Y
10 Area = 100 60 Area = ?
A 10 D W 60 Z

25. Find the volume of the cube. _____

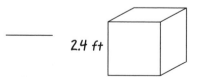

2.4 ft

DECIMALS

Write the value of the 6 in each number.

1. 31.486 _____

2. 821.063 _____

Fill in the blanks with the correct symbol, < (less than) or > (greater than).

3. 9.982 _____ 14.1

4. 813.913 _____ 813.899

Round the number to the nearest hundredth.

5. 812.304 _____

6. 1.9059 _____

Rewrite the number as directed.

7. Write 64.375 as a fraction in simplest form. _____

8. Write $5\frac{5}{9}$ as a decimal. _____

9. Jeff measured the distance from his front door to the street. From the front door to the bottom of the steps was 1.65 m. From the steps to the driveway was 3.2 m. From the driveway to the street was 7.85 m. Estimate the total distance from the front door to the street. Then find the actual distance.

Estimate: _____   Actual distance: _____

10. Ae Ri's class had a recycling drive. On the first day, the class earned $10.44, on the second day, $5.75, and on the third day, $3.33. How much did the class earn for the three days? _____

11. A restaurant had two partly filled bags of flour. One weighed 537 grams. The other weighed 2.7 kilograms. What was their combined weight? _____

Find the difference.

12.   30.12
    − 2.41

13. From 4.3 km subtract 953 m.   _____

14. Carlos had $318.73 in his savings account. He withdrew $42.18 to buy a present for his wife's birthday. How much did Carlos have left in the account? _____

Multiply to find the answers to these problems.

15. 5.47
× 10

16. 5.418
× .53

17. Stacy pays her sales department employees $7.49 per hour. The workweek is 38 hours. Estimate how much Stacy pays each employee for 1 week. Then find the actual amount.

Estimate: _____   Actual amount: _____

18. Sung wants to cover the bedroom floor while he paints the room. The room measures 6.41 m long and 4.83 m wide. How much area, in square meters, must Sung cover? _____

Divide to find the answers to these problems.

19. $1000\overline{)1{,}457.4}$

20. $19\overline{)985.53}$

21. Enrique bought 3.25 pounds of apples for $2.89. Estimate how much the apples cost per pound. Then find the actual cost. Round to the nearest cent.

Estimate: _____   Actual cost: _____

22. Mi Lin wants to tile her bathroom floor. Each tile is 15.24 cm long. If her bathroom measures 3.6 m long, how many tiles will it take to make one row the length of the room? Round to the nearest whole number. _____

Write the decimal as a percent.

Write the percent as a decimal.

23. 1.8 = _____%

24. 10.3% = _____

25. Chad and his wife had dinner at their favorite restaurant. The bill came to $22.96. How much money should Chad give to the waitress for a tip if he wants to leave a 15% tip? Round to the nearest cent. _____

DECIMALS

Write the value of the 3 in each number.

1. 68.931 _____

2. 710.35 _____

Fill in the blanks with the correct symbol, < (less than) or > (greater than).

3. 4.156 _____ 3.902

4. 90.8315 _____ 101.3

Round the number to the nearest hundredth.

5. 34.0983 _____

6. 0.8149 _____

Rewrite the number as directed.

7. Write 21.125 as a fraction in simplest form. _____

8. Write $7\frac{3}{7}$ as a decimal. Round to the nearest thousandth if necessary. _____

9. Mark drove 10.49 km making his first delivery in the company van. His second stop was 8.12 km from the first stop. It took him an additional 15.83 km to get back to the office. Estimate the total distance that Mark drove. Then find the actual distance.

Estimate: _____   Actual distance: _____

10. Karina earned spending money working at her uncle's store. On Friday, she earned $13.78; on Saturday, $24.19; and on Sunday, $28.42. How much did she earn for the three days? _____

11. For an Iron Woman race, Lacey ran 1500 meters and bicycled 12.4 kilometers. How much distance did she cover for this race? _____

Find the difference.

12.   13.871
        − 4.58

13. From 1.4 kilograms subtract 519 grams. _____

14. Jose treated his employees to lunch. The total bill came to $46.13. He gave the cashier $60. How much change should Jose get back? _____

Multiply to find the answers to these problems.

15.   6.19
    $\times$ 100

16.   18.93
    $\times$ 4.27

17. Lee got a raise to $8.35 per hour at her office job. She works 45 hours per week. Estimate how much Lee earns in a week. Then find the actual amount.

Estimate: _____   Actual amount: _____

18. Cau measured his living room to find out how much carpeting he needed. The room was 5.3 m long and 4.79 m wide. What was the area of Cau's living room in square meters? _____

Divide to find the answers to these problems.

19. 100)¯39.392

20. 24)¯1500.96

21. Raul bought 8.5 pounds of chicken for $5.85. Estimate the cost per pound for the chicken. Then find the actual cost. Round to the nearest tenth.

Estimate: _____   Actual cost: _____

22. Angela uses 8.3 cm of masking tape to hang each poster in her room. She has a roll of tape measuring 135.8 cm. How many posters can Angela hang? Round to the nearest whole number. _____

Write the decimal as a percent.

23. .419 = _____ %

Write the percent as a decimal.

24. 8.5% = _____

25. Jason earns $387.38 per week. He puts 5% of his earnings in a savings account. How much does Jason save per week? Round to the nearest cent. _____

1. Shade 40% of the figure.

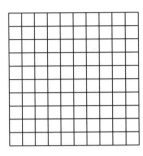

2. Write 39% as a decimal. _____

3. Write .92 as a percent. _____

4. Write $1\frac{4}{5}$ as a percent. _____

5. Write 12.5% as a fraction in simplest form. _____

Solve the following problems.

6. 12.5 % of 182 = _____

7. 72% of 16 = _____

8. _____% of 400 = 25

9. _____% of 6 = 1.5

10. 2% of what number is 6? _____

11. 60% of what number is 36? _____

12. A CD that usually sells for $16.95 is selling for 20% off. How much will it cost? Round to the nearest cent. _____

13. A radio with a list price of $82.15 is selling for 33% off. What is the discount price of the radio? Round to the nearest cent. _____

14. Corliss bought art supplies for $15.50. If sales tax is 7.5%, how much tax will she pay? Round to the nearest cent. _____

15. Darren buys clothing that costs $78.24 before tax. Sales tax is 7%. How much will he pay including tax? Round to the nearest cent. _____

16. Youssef borrowed $239. He agreed to repay the loan at a simple interest rate of 6% over 3 years. How much interest will Youssef owe? Round to the nearest cent. _____

17. Marla took out a loan of $400 for 2 years with a simple interest rate of 4.5%. How much did Marla pay back, including interest, at the end of the loan? Round to the nearest cent. _____

18. Eun-ji deposits $500 in a savings account. The interest rate is 5%, compounded yearly. If she leaves the deposit in for 2 years, how much interest will she have at the end of that period? Round to the nearest cent. _____

19. Of 194 students in the dance club, 72 signed up for the recital. Estimate the percent of students who signed up. Then find the actual percent. Round to the nearest tenth of a percent.

Estimate: _____   Actual percent: _____

20. Juan paid $89.21 for groceries. If he had not used coupons, the groceries would have cost $96.70. Find the discount rate Juan got for using coupons. Round to the nearest whole percent. _____

21. The list price of a fan is $59.95. Sales tax is $4.20. What is the tax rate? Round to the nearest whole percent. _____

Use the tax table to solve questions 22–23.

22. Janette, who is single, earned $28,915 in taxable income during 1994. What is her approximate tax rate?

_____

23. Maria and Jorge earned $28,848 in taxable income during 1994. They are married and file jointly. What is their approximate tax rate?

_____

Tax Table

If taxable income is—		And you are—			
At least	But less than	Single	Married filing jointly	Married filing separately	Head of a household
		Your tax is—			
28,000	28,850	5,114	4,324	5,601	4,324
28,850	28,900	5,128	4,331	5,615	4,331
28,900	28,950	5,142	4,339	5,629	4,339
28,950	29,000	5,156	4,346	5,643	4,346

24. Ariana has knitted 105 squares. This is 75% of the squares she will need for an afghan. How many squares will be in the afghan? _____

25. Larry bought 3 reams of paper for his copier. Each ream has a list price of $4.97. The paper is on sale at 10% off. The state sales tax rate is 7%. How much will the paper cost Larry? Round to the nearest cent. _____

PERCENTS

1. Shade 15% of the figure.

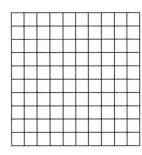

2. Write 16.7% as a decimal. _____

3. Write .4 as a percent. _____

4. Write $1\frac{1}{8}$ as a percent. _____

5. Write 160% as a fraction in simplest form. _____

Solve the following problems.

6. 32% of 96 = _____

7. 8.2% of 240 = _____

8. _____% of 560 = 14

9. _____% of 16 = 3.2

10. 80% of what number is 55? _____

11. 4% of what number is 3.25? _____

12. A sweater is selling for 15% off. Its list price is $24. What is the sale price? Round to the nearest cent. _____

13. A coupon gives 12% off on dinner at Ben's Restaurant. If a meal normally costs $18.62, what will it cost with the coupon? Round to the nearest cent. _____

14. Eva buys a printer costing $385.97. If sales tax is 6%, how much tax will she pay? Round to the nearest cent. _____

15. Arturo buys a videocassette costing $17.99 before tax. Sales tax is 8.5%. How much will Arturo pay including tax? Round to the nearest cent. _____

16. Bill borrowed $239 to repair his car. He must repay the loan at a simple interest rate of 5% over 2 years. How much interest will Bill owe? Round to the nearest cent. _____

17. Sonia took out a loan of $397 for 3 years. The simple interest rate was 4.5%. How much did Sonia pay back, including interest, at the end of the loan? Round to the nearest cent.

_____

18. Luz bought a CD (certificate of deposit) for $500. The interest rate is 6%, compounded yearly. After 3 years, how much interest will she have? Round to the nearest cent.

_____

19. Midvale's population is 6,321. Only 54 people have lived in Midvale less than a year. Estimate the percent of the population that has lived there less than a year. Then find the actual percent. Round to the nearest tenth of a percent.

Estimate: _____   Actual percent: _____

20. Tomoko paid $62.30 for boots that regularly cost $75. Find the discount rate that she got for the boots. Round to the nearest whole percent.

_____

21. Ty pays $1.52 in sales tax on a book whose price is $23.45. What is the tax rate? Round to the nearest whole percent.

_____

Use the tax table to solve questions 22–23.

22. Elisa is a head of household. She earned $53,210 in taxable income during 1994. What is her approximate tax rate?

_____

Tax Table

If taxable income is—		And you are—			
At least	But less than	Single	Married filing jointly	Married filing separately	Head of a household
			Your tax is—		
53,200	53,250	11,946	9,963	12,652	10,938
53,250	53,300	11,960	9,977	12,668	10,952
53,300	53,350	11,974	9,991	12,683	10,966
53,350	53,400	11,988	10,005	12,699	10,980

23. Andrea and Chou earned $53,315 in taxable income during 1994. They are married and file separately. What is their approximate tax rate? _____

24. At a book fair, Harry has sold 250 books. This is 40% of all the books he started out with in his booth. How many books did he start out with? _____

25. Lucy buys 2 suits with a list price of $109.50 each. The suits are on sale at 15% off. The state sales tax rate is 8%. How much will Lucy pay? Round to the nearest cent.

_____

Rename each measurement.

1. 33 ft = _____ yd

2. 4.5 ft = _____ in.

3. 12 qt = _____ gal

4. 2.5 c = _____ oz

5. 3.5 lb = _____ oz

6. 5,000 lb = _____ T

7. 0.82 m = _____ cm

8. 12,690 mL = _____ L

9. 1.43 kg = _____ g

Use the triangle to answer questions 10–11.

10. Find the measure of the exterior angle next to angle A. _____

11. Find the measure of the interior angle B. _____

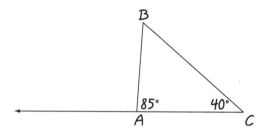

Use the parallelogram to answer questions 12–13.

12. Find the measure of angle P. _____

13. Find the sum of angle P and angle S. _____

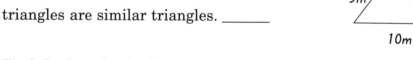

14. Find the length of side a if these two triangles are similar triangles. _____

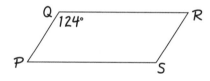

15. Find the length of side c in the right triangle. _____

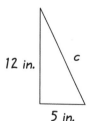

Use the diagram to solve problems 16–21.

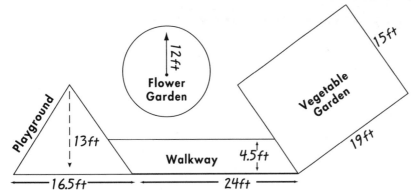

16. The Takinos decide to place a fence around the rectangular vegetable garden. How many feet of fencing will they need? _____

17. The Takinos have to fertilize the vegetable garden. Find the vegetable garden's area. _____

18. The Takinos have a triangular playground for their children. Find the area of the playground. _____

19. The walkway in the Takinos' backyard forms a parallelogram. To pave the walkway, the Takinos must buy concrete. Find the area of the walkway. _____

20. Find the circumference of the circular flower garden in the Takinos' backyard. _____

21. The Takinos want to cover the flower garden with tarp. Find the area of the flower garden. _____

Use the coordinate plane to answer problems 22–25.

22. What kind of triangle is formed by points D, B, and E? _____

23. Find the area of the rectangle formed by points C, B, D, and F. _____

24. The rectangle formed by points C, B, D, and F is flipped over the x-axis. Find the coordinates of point F after the figure is flipped. _____

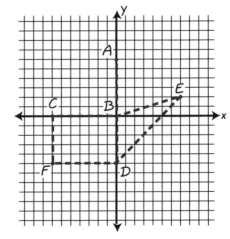

25. What are the coordinates of points C, B, D, and F if you slide the rectangle 4 units horizontally to the right? _____

MEASUREMENT AND GEOMETRY

Rename each measurement.

1. 1.5 ft = _____ in.

2. 27 ft = _____ yd

3. 6 qt = _____ gal

4. 3 c = _____ oz

5. 2.5 lb = _____ oz

6. 3,000 lb = _____ T

7. 4.32 m = _____ cm

8. 1,746 mL = _____ L

9. 6.7 kg = _____ g

Use the triangle to answer questions 10–11.

10. Find the measure of the exterior angle next to angle A. _____

11. Find the measure of the interior angle B. _____

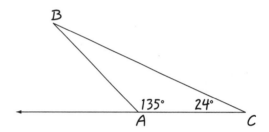

Use the parallelogram to answer questions 12–13.

12. Find the measure of angle P. _____

13. Find the sum of angle P and angle S. _____

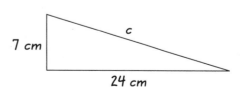

14. Find the length of side *a* if these two triangles are similar triangles. _____

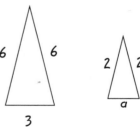

15. Find the length of side *c* in the right triangle. _____

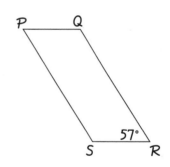

Use the diagram to solve problems 16–21.

16. The Bellmans decide to place a fence around the 2 sides of the lawn not bordered by the house. How many feet of fencing will they need? _____

17. The Bellmans want to waterproof the deck, which is a square. Find the area of the deck. _____

18. Find the area of the triangular lawn that the Bellmans will have to cover with lawn seed. _____

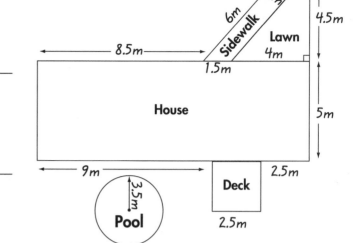

19. The sidewalk of the Bellmans' house forms a parallelogram. To pave the sidewalk, the Bellmans must buy concrete. Find the area of the sidewalk. _____

20. Find the circumference of the circular swimming pool in the Bellmans' backyard. _____

21. The Bellmans need a pool cover. Find the area of their pool. _____

Use the coordinate plane to answer problems 22–25.

22. What kind of triangle is formed by points A, B, and D? _____

23. Find the area of the triangle formed by points A, B, and C. _____

24. The parallelogram formed by points A, B, E, and C is flipped over the x-axis. Find the coordinates of point C after the figure is flipped. _____

25. What are the coordinates of points A, B, E, and C if you slide the parallelogram 3 units horizontally to the left?

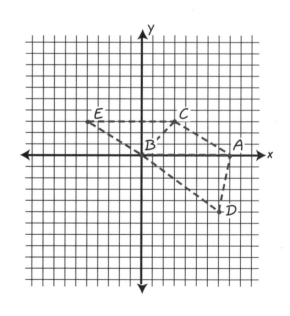

_____

ESTIMATION

1. Tell whether an exact value or an estimate is more appropriate for this situation: paying a monthly telephone bill. _____

2. Round each number to the underlined place value.

   4,599 _____   4,199 _____   22,420 _____

3. Use mental math to add these numbers: $52 + 21 + 18 =$ _____

4. Yolanda ordered lunch at her favorite fast food restaurant. She had a cheeseburger for $2.81, french fries for $0.92, and a lemonade for $0.49. About how much did she spend? _____

5. In 1994, there were 9,384,512 people unemployed in the U.S. Of those, 8,027,947 were seeking work. Estimate the number of unemployed who were not seeking work. _____

6. The table shows the number of rainy days during the rainy season. Estimate the average number of rainy days per month.

Month	June	July	August
Number of Rainy Days	28	22	29

   _____

7. Round 43.9094 to the nearest thousandth. _____

8. Tae shopped for some groceries. She bought the following:

Cereal	$2.39	Butter	$1.29	Dog food	$5.99
Ice cream	$2.59	Detergent	$2.49	Pork chops	$1.79

   Estimate the cost of Tae's purchases. _____

9. Estimate the sum of these numbers: 16.12, 5.39, 14.99, 34.05, 8.41, 11.30, 25.84 _____

10. Estimate the difference between these numbers: $12.182 - 7.893$ _____

11. Use mental math to find the answers:

8×500 _____ 30×11 _____ 5×87 _____

12. Belinda ordered 49 square yards of carpeting that cost $15 per square yard. Estimate how much the carpet will cost and tell whether you overestimated or underestimated. _____

13. Jim produced 318 parts during a 40-hour week. About how many parts did Jim produce each hour? _____

14. Estimate the product of 43.7×4.28. _____

15. Estimate the quotient of $479.03 \div 24$. _____

16. Estimate the sum of these fractions: $\frac{7}{8} + \frac{2}{5} + \frac{5}{6}$. _____

17. Estimate the sum of these mixed numbers by rounding the fractions to the nearest half unit: $7\frac{5}{8} + 5\frac{3}{4} + 12\frac{1}{5}$. _____

18. Estimate the difference of these mixed numbers by rounding the fractions to the nearest half unit: $18\frac{3}{8} - 7\frac{5}{9}$. _____

19. Estimate each product. $5\frac{1}{4} \times 3\frac{4}{5}$ _____ $2\frac{1}{2} \times 3\frac{1}{3}$ _____

20. Estimate the area of this figure. Then find the exact area.

Estimate: _____   Exact: _____

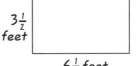

$3\frac{1}{2}$ feet

$6\frac{1}{4}$ feet

21. Estimate the area of this irregular shape. _____

22. Estimate what percent of the second figure is shaded. _____

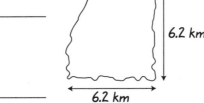

6.2 km

6.2 km

23. Mr. Flores typed 65% of his report. The report is 72 pages long. About how many pages has he typed? _____

24. Estimate the percent for each ratio.

83 out of 98 _____   3 out of 6 _____   24 out of 99 _____

25. Bo drove 183 miles to see a concert. His car averages 28 miles per gallon. Estimate the cost of gasoline if Bo spends $1.08 per gallon. _____

ESTIMATION

1. Tell whether an exact value or an estimate is more appropriate for this situation: planning the time it takes to get to work.

   _____

2. Round each number to the underlined place value.

   14,6̲52 _____   2̲,560 _____   8̲,221 _____

3. Use mental math to add these numbers: 43 + 19 + 27 = _____

4. Paula drove for three days to get to her friend's house. She drove 387 miles, 421 miles, and 272 miles. Estimate the total number of miles Paula drove.   _____

5. In 1980 there were 226,542,203 people living in the U.S. In 1970, the population was 203,302,031. Estimate the increase in population.   _____

6. The table shows how many points Cecil scored in seven games. Estimate the average score for Cecil.

Game Number	1	2	3	4	5	6	7
Number of Points	23	28	39	44	12	27	36

   _____

7. Round 13.836 to the nearest hundredth. _____

8. Nathan shopped for some groceries. He bought the following:

eggs $1.79	coffee $3.95	bread $1.92
juice $1.39	yogurt $0.88	bacon $1.39

   Estimate the cost of Nathan's purchases. _____

9. Estimate the sum of these numbers:
   12.53, 8.39, 34.51, 16.93, 4.21, 10.04, 6.71, 13.91   _____

10. Estimate the difference between these numbers: 6.432 − 3.501   _____

11. Use mental math to find the answers:

    4 × 50 _____   20 × 12 _____   4 × 62 _____

12. Sally works part-time at a book store for $11 per hour. She works 32 hours per week. Estimate how much Sally earns and tell if you overestimated or underestimated. _____

13. The science textbook has 31 lines and 240 words on each page. About how many words are on each line? _____

14. Estimate the product of 12.24 × 5.81. _____

15. Estimate the quotient of 641.33 ÷ 16. _____

16. Estimate the sum of these fractions: $\frac{4}{5} + \frac{1}{6} + \frac{1}{3}$. _____

17. Estimate the sum of these mixed numbers by rounding the fractions to the nearest half unit: $4\frac{2}{5} + 10\frac{1}{8} + 3\frac{6}{7}$. _____

18. Estimate the difference of these mixed numbers by rounding the fractions to the nearest half unit: $14\frac{1}{6} - 8\frac{7}{8}$. _____

19. Estimate each product.

$4\frac{3}{4} \times 4\frac{3}{5}$ _____ $2\frac{1}{4} \times 4\frac{1}{3}$ _____

20. Estimate the area of this figure. Then find the exact area.

Estimate: _____   Exact: _____

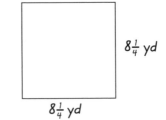

$8\frac{1}{4}$ yd

$8\frac{1}{4}$ yd

21. Estimate the area of this irregular shape. _____

22. Estimate what percent of the second figure is shaded. _____

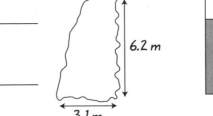

6.2 m

3.1 m

23. 34% of Mr. Morales' social studies class received A's on their first quiz. There are 35 students in the class. Estimate how many students got an A. _____

24. Estimate the percent for each ratio.

35 out of 102 _____   2 out of 8 _____

25. Joel drove 110 miles to visit his sister. His car averages 30 miles per gallon. Estimate the cost of gas if he spends $1.05 per gallon. _____

GRAPHING AND INTERPRETING DATA

Use the graph to solve problems 1–3.

1. Which city saw a decrease in the median price of a single-family home from April 1992 to April 1994? _____

2. About how much more did a home in Salt Lake City cost in April 1994 than it did in April 1992? _____

3. Add the following data to the graph.

City	April 1992	April 1994
Syracuse, NY	$77,000	$82,000

Prices of Homes

Use the pictograph to solve problems 4–5.

4. How many dachshunds are registered? _____

5. 100,000 Rottweilers are registered. Figure out how many symbols to use on the pictograph and add the information to the graph. _____

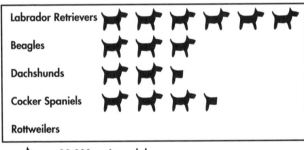

Use the circle graph to solve problems 6–8.

6. About 17.8 qBtu's (quadrillion British thermal units) of natural gas are produced. Find the percent of energy production natural gas represents. Round to the nearest percent. _____

7. What fractional part of energy production comes from crude oil? _____

8. Find the angle needed to draw the segment for nuclear energy. Round to the nearest degree. _____

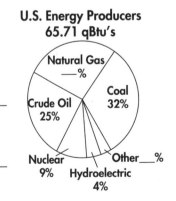

U.S. Energy Producers
65.71 qBtu's

Scores by 49 Students on 50-Problem Math Test

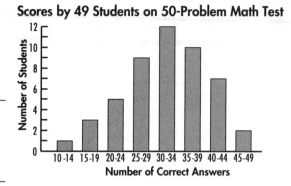

9. Find the number of students that
scored from 35 to 39 correct answers
on the math test. _____

10. The total of all of the scores on the
math test was 1,560. What is the mean
score? Round to the nearest tenth. _____

11. What is the mode score range for the math test? _____

12. What is the median score range for the math test? _____

**Use the stem-and-leaf plot
to solve problems 13–14.**

Student Test Scores

8	0 5 2 9 7
9	9 1 3 8

13. Show the number 96 on the stem-and-leaf plot.

14. How many students scored from 80 to 90? _____

Use the graph to solve problems 15–16.

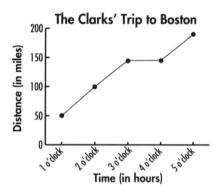
The Clarks' Trip to Boston

15. How many hours did it take the
Clarks to drive 150 miles? _____

16. When did the Clarks stop for
lunch? _____

Use the grid to solve problems 17–18.

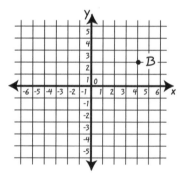

17. What ordered pair gives the location of Point B? _____

18. Use these ordered pairs to draw points for
C, D, and E.

Point C: (3,1)   Point D: (⁻2,3)   Point E: (4,⁻2)

19. Find the ordered pair that is the solution of
the linear equation $y = 4x - 3$, when $x = 3$. _____

20. List the positive solutions for $x + y = 6$. _____

GRAPHING AND INTERPRETING DATA

Use the graph to solve problems 1–3.

1. About what was the increase in the number of computers sold between 1993 and 1994? _____

2. In which year were there CD-ROMs in 10% of U.S. households? _____

3. Add the following data from the table to the graph.

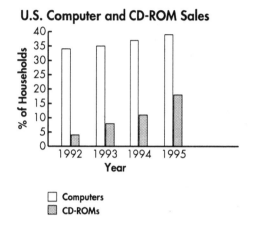

U.S. Computer and CD-ROM Sales

□ Computers
▨ CD-ROMs

Percentage Projections for 1996			
Computers	43%	CD-ROMs	24%

Use the pictograph to solve problems 4–5.

4. About how many qBtu's (quadrillion British thermal units) of primary energy are produced by the United States? _____

5. About 7 qBtu's are produced by Italy. Decide how many symbols to use on the pictograph and then add the information to the graph. _____

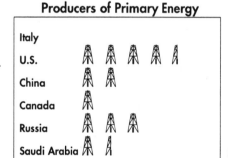

Producers of Primary Energy

Italy
U.S.
China
Canada
Russia
Saudi Arabia

🗼 = 15 qBTU's

Use the circle graph to solve problems 6–8.

6. 18.7 qBtu's of coal are consumed in the United States. Find the percent of energy consumption that coal represents. Round to the nearest percent. _____

7. How many qBtu's of energy consumption come from petroleum products? _____

8. Find the angle needed to draw the segment for hydroelectric energy. Round to the nearest degree. _____

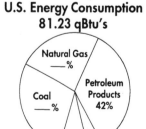

U.S. Energy Consumption
81.23 qBtu's

Natural Gas —%
Petroleum Products 42%
Coal —%
Nuclear 7%
Hydroelectric 4%

Use the histogram to solve problems 9–12.

9. Find the number of students that scored 9 correct answers on the science test. _____

10. The total of all the test scores was 310. Find the mean score for the test. Round to the nearest tenth. _____

11. Find the mode score for the test. _____

12. Find the median score for the test. _____

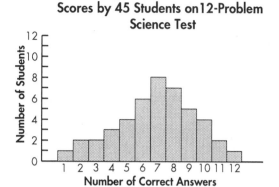

Scores by 45 Students on 12-Problem Science Test

Number of Students / Number of Correct Answers

Use the stem-and-leaf plot to solve problems 13–14.

13. Show the number 82 on the stem-and-leaf plot.

14. How many students scored from 70 to 80? _____

Student Test Scores

| 7 | 8 9 8 4 2 8 |
| 8 | 8 4 0 3 1 |

Use the graph to solve problems 15–16.

15. How many hours did it take the Luckeys to drive the first 100 miles? _____

16. About how many miles per hour are the Luckeys driving? _____

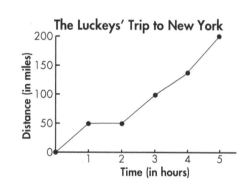

The Luckeys' Trip to New York

Distance (in miles) / Time (in hours)

Use the grid to solve problems 17–18.

17. What ordered pair gives the location of Point D? _____

18. Use these ordered pairs to draw points for E, F, and G.

Point E: (⁻3, ⁻2)   Point F: (4,3)   Point G: (2,⁻5)

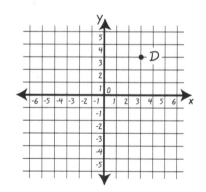

19. Find the ordered pair that is a solution of the linear equation $y = 3x - 2$ when $x = 4$. _____

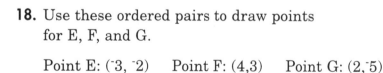

20. List the positive solutions for $x + y = 8$. _____

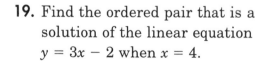

■ BASIC STATISTICS

Use the table to solve problem 1.

Number of Pages Buddy Typed at Job

Monday	Tuesday	Wednesday	Thursday	Friday
58	47	84	62	47

1. What is the mean for the number of pages Buddy typed? _____

   the median? _____   the range? _____   the mode? _____

Use the bar graph to solve problems 2–3.

2. What is the mean for the top speeds of the animals? Round to the nearest whole number. _____

3. Add the following data to the graph: the top speed for a quarterhorse is 47.5 mph.

Top Speeds of Animals

Use the pictograph to solve problems 4–5.

4. How many more houses were built in 1994 than 1995? _____

5. Which years represent the mode? _____

Homes Built in Cole County (1990–1995)

= 100 homes

Use the frequency table to solve problems 6–7.

6. Which price occurs most frequently? _____

7. How many stores were surveyed? _____

Telephone Survey of Frozen Yogurt Prices

Price	Tally	Frequency
$1.50	II	2
$1.75	₶₶ I	6
$2.00	IIII	4
$2.25	III	3

8. Lucy had 5 hits in 15 times at bat. What is her batting average?

_____ rounded to three places.

Use the circle graph to solve problems 9–10.

9. The Bradleys' monthly expenses are $1,545. What is the dollar amount for food? _____

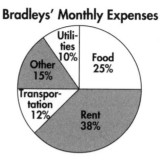
Bradleys' Monthly Expenses

10. If utilities expenses represent 10% of the whole, what part of the circle represents this amount?

_____ degrees

Use the line graph to solve problems 11–13.

11. About how much did a worker earn in 1988? _____

12. Predict what the earnings for a worker will be in 1997, and add the data to the graph. _____

13. What conclusions can you draw about earnings over the past 30 years from reading this graph?

_____

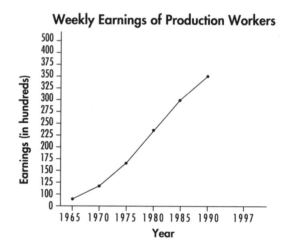
Weekly Earnings of Production Workers

14. In a recent public opinion poll, 45% of those questioned believed that their standard of living improved during the past year. The reliability of the poll was + or − 7%. Find the highest percent that falls within the range.

_____

15. The ad at the right appeared in a magazine: What is misleading about this ad?

_____

Only $1.95 per minute
Average call — 10 minutes

16. In 1990, 1.5 per 100,000 women died of skin cancer. In a city in which there are about 500,000 women, about how many women would you expect to have died from skin cancer in 1990?

_____

BASIC STATISTICS

Use the table to solve problem 1.

Number of Telephone Inquiries Nikki Took

Monday	Tuesday	Wednesday	Thursday	Friday
130	385	294	385	305

1. What is the mean for the number of inquiries Nikki took? _____

   the median? _____   the range? _____   the mode? _____

Use the bar graph to solve problems 2-3.

2. What is the mean for the state
   sales taxes?   _____

3. Add the following data to the graph:
   the New York State sales tax is $8\frac{1}{4}\%$.
   Round to the nearest whole number.

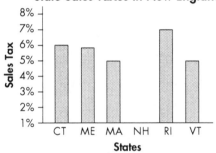

State Sales Taxes in New England

Use the pictograph to solve problems 4-5.

4. How much more traffic was there
   in Dallas/Ft. Worth than Miami?   _____

5. Which cities represent the mode?

   _____

Traffic at U.S. Airports (1993)

Chicago (O'Hare)	✈ ✈ ✈ ⸰
Dallas/Ft. Worth	✈ ✈ ⸱
Miami	✈ ⸱
Los Angeles	✈ ✈ ⸱
Houston	✈

✈ = 20 million passengers

Use the frequency table to solve
problems 6-7.

6. Which response was chosen by the
   most students?   _____

7. How many students chose jazz
   music?   _____

Student Survey of Favorite Music

Response	Tally	Frequency
Pop	III	3
Rap	I	1
R&B	HHT II	7
Jazz	HHT	5

8. Jake had 4 hits in 16 times at bat. What is his batting average?

_____ rounded to three places

Use the circle graph to solve problems 9–10.

9. How many votes did Rodriguez get? _____

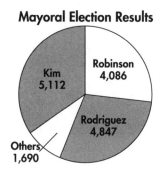

Mayoral Election Results

Kim 5,112

Robinson 4,086

Rodriguez 4,847

Others 1,690

10. If Robinson got about 30% of the vote, what part of the circle represents this amount?

_____ degrees

Use the line graph to solve problems 11–13.

11. In which year was the unemployment rate the lowest? _____

12. About how much could you expect the unemployment rate to change in either direction for 1994?

_____

U.S. Unemployment Rate

% of Population Unemployed

8
7.75
7.5
7.25
7
6.75
6.5
6.25
6
5.75
5.5
5.25
5
0

1985 1986 1987 1988 1989 1990 1991 1992 1993

Year

13. What conclusions can you draw about the unemployment rate over the 8 years?

_____

14. In a recent public opinion poll, 57% of the voters thought that their governor was doing a good job. The reliability of the poll was + or − 3%. Find the lowest percent that is within the range. _____

15. An advertisement in a magazine claimed the following:

What is misleading about this ad?

_____

100% DAILY REQUIREMENT of iron in EVERY 12-oz box

(Serving size 2 oz)

16. In 1990, 20 per 100,000 men died of colon cancer. In a city in which there are about 800,000 men, about how many men would you expect to have died from colon cancer in 1990? _____

PROBABILITY

1. A 6-sided number cube contains the numbers 1 through 6. Find the number of outcomes that can occur when the cube is tossed. _____

2. Find the probability, or ratio of a specific outcome to all possible outcomes, that the cube will land with the number 3 on top. _____

3. A deck of 52 cards is divided into 4 suits: hearts, spades, diamonds, and clubs. Each suit has an ace, king, queen, jack, 10, 9, 8, 7, 6, 5, 4, 3, and 2. Find the number of outcomes that can occur when a card is chosen from the deck. _____

4. Find the probability that the jack of spades will be chosen from the deck. _____

5. Danielle flipped a coin 3 times. List all the possible outcomes. _____

6. Find the probability of exactly 2 heads being flipped in 3 flips. _____

7. Ae Ri rolled a 6-sided number cube containing the numbers 1 through 6. Find the probability that she will roll a number greater than 6. _____

8. The probability of Alex winning his office pool is 1 out of 25. Find the probability that he will *not* win the pool. _____

9. Ten numbers between 1 and 50 were selected at random: 38, 29, 4, 15, 6, 45, 31, 20, 5, 11. Find the relative frequency (or ratio of a specific outcome to an existing set of outcomes) of an odd number. _____

10. Find the relative frequency of an even number. _____

11. Find the relative frequency of a number greater than 40. _____

12. A sample of 18,000 people were asked their opinions about national issues. The sample represents 1% of the population. Find the population that the sample represents. _____

13. Write the probability of "a 75% chance of rain" as a ratio. Is the event likely or unlikely to occur? _____

14. Marla spins a spinner with 8 equal areas, numbered 1 through 8. Find the probability that she will spin an even number or a 5 on the spinner. _____

Use the tree diagram to solve problems 15–16.

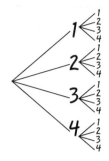

15. Find the probability that a 1 is rolled on a 4-sided number pyramid containing the numbers 1 through 4. _____

16. Find the probability that a 4 comes up on the first roll and an even number comes up on the second roll of the pyramid. _____

17. Kirsten rolls two 4-sided number pyramids. Find the probability that she will roll an even number on each pyramid. _____

18. Find the probability that Kirsten will roll a 2 or better on each 4-sided number pyramid. _____

19. From a bowl containing 24 balls numbered 1 through 24, two balls have been selected: a 24 and a 12. Find the probability that the third ball selected will be greater than 19. _____

20. Two balls are randomly selected from a bowl containing 24 balls numbered 1 through 24. Find the probability that the balls are drawn in this order: 24, 12. _____

Use the dart board to solve problems 21–22.

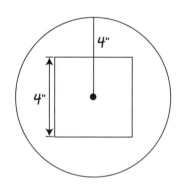

21. Find the probability that a dart randomly tossed that hits the dartboard will land in the square. _____

22. Find the probability that a dart randomly tossed that hits the dartboard will land in the circle, but not in the square. _____

23. In how many ways can 5 books be arranged on a shelf? _____

24. In how many ways can you arrange 4 things taken 3 at a time? _____

25. Find the number of possible combinations of 3 letters from the letters A, B, C, and D. _____

1. Find the number of outcomes that can occur when the spinner is spun. _____

2. Find the probability, or ratio of a specific outcome to all possible outcomes, that the spinner will stop on the number 7. _____

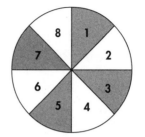

3. One hundred tickets are sold in a school lottery. One ticket will be chosen as the winner. Find the number of outcomes that can occur when a ticket is chosen. _____

4. Johan bought 1 ticket in the school lottery. Find the probability that his ticket will be chosen. _____

5. Find the probability that a ticket with a number of 1 through 100 will be chosen. _____

6. The probability that Lucia will win the lottery is 1/50. Find the probability that Lucia will not win the lottery. _____

7. A 4-sided number pyramid shows the numbers 1 through 4. Al rolls the pyramid twice. List all of the possible outcomes. _____

8. Find the probability of Al's rolling an even number and then an odd number. _____

9. Ten numbers between 1 and 20 are selected at random: 2, 17, 15, 9, 8, 1, 5, 12, 18, 3. Find the relative frequency (or ratio of a specific outcome to existing set of outcomes) of a number greater than 10. _____

10. Find the relative frequency of an even number. _____

11. Find the relative frequency of a number evenly divisible by 3. _____

12. A sample of 15,000 people were asked their opinions about national issues. The sample represents 1.5% of the population. Find the population that the sample represents. _____

13. Write the probability of "a 25% chance of rain" as a ratio. Is the event likely or unlikely to happen? _____

14. Tom rolls a 4-sided number pyramid containing the numbers 1 through 4. Find the probability of his rolling an odd number or a 2. _____

Use the tree diagram to solve problems 15–16.

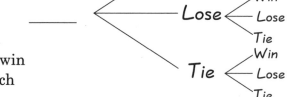

15. Find the probability that the Kickers soccer team will win their first game against a team with which they are evenly matched. _____

16. Find the probability that the team will win one and tie one against teams with which they are evenly matched. _____

17. Esteban tosses four coins once. Find the probability that he will get 4 heads. _____

18. Esteban tosses four coins twice. Find the probability that the first toss will result in 4 tails and the second toss will result in anything but 4 tails. _____

19. Two cards are drawn from a deck of 52 cards that contains ace, king, queen, jack, and 2 through 10 in four suits (hearts, clubs, diamonds, and spades). The first card is a 2 of diamonds. Find the probability that the second card drawn will be a 2 of another suit. _____

20. Andrea has drawn 3 cards from the full deck described in problem 19. Find the probability that she will draw a spade followed by a diamond. _____

Use the dart board to solve problems 21–22.

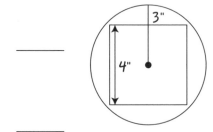

21. Find the probability that a dart randomly tossed that hits the dartboard will land in the square. _____

22. Find the probability that a dart randomly tossed that hits the dartboard will land in the circle, but not in the square. _____

23. In how many ways can 6 birds sit in a row? _____

24. In how many ways can you arrange 5 things taken 3 at a time? _____

25. Find the number of combinations of choosing 2 colored cards from 4 cards of different colors. _____

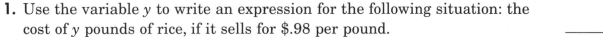
1. Use the variable y to write an expression for the following situation: the cost of y pounds of rice, if it sells for \$.98 per pound. _____

2. Simplify the expression. $(2t + 3t) \div 2$ _____

3. Find the value of the expression for the given variable.

   $2a + 5a \div 3; a = 3$ _____

4. Solve for a. $5a + 16 = 73$ _____   5. Solve for a. $a \times 2b = c$ _____

Use the formulas provided to solve problems 6–10.

6. $d = rt$; solve for t when $d = 67.2$ mi and $r = 42$ mph _____

7. $C = \frac{5}{9}(F - 32)$; solve for F when $C = 28$. Round to the nearest degree. _____

8. $i = prt$; solve for r when $t = 3$ years, $p = \$500$, and $i = \$93$ _____

9. sales tax = rate × price; total cost = price + sales tax; solve for total cost when price = \$19.99 and rate = 8.25%. Round to the nearest cent. _____

10. discount = rate × original price; final cost = original price − discount. Find the total cost when original price = \$6.99 and rate of discount = 25%. _____

11. Find the perimeter of the rectangle using the formula:
    $perimeter = 2 \times length + 2 \times width$. _____

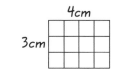

12. Find the area of the rectangle using the formula: $area = length \times width$. _____

13. Find the circumference of the circle using the formula: $circumference = 2\pi r$, where $\pi = \frac{22}{7}$ and $r = 6$. _____

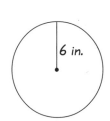

14. Find the area of the circle using the formula: $area = \pi r^2$, where $\pi = 3.14$ and $r = $ radius. Round to the nearest tenth. _____

15. Find the area of a parallelogram with a height of $4\frac{3}{4}$ cm and a base of $2\frac{1}{2}$ cm. The formula is: *area = base × height.*

_____

16. Find the area of a triangle with a base of 5.6 in. and a height of 4.8 in. The formula is: area = $\frac{1}{2}$ *base × height.*

_____

Use the figures to solve problems 17–20.

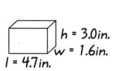  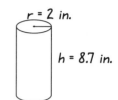

17. Using the formula *volume of prism = lwh*, find the volume of the prism, rounded to the nearest tenth.

_____

18. Using the formula *volume of cone* = $\frac{1}{3}\pi r^2 h$, find the volume of the cone, rounded to the nearest tenth. Use 3.14 for π.

_____

19. Using the formula *volume of pyramid* = $\frac{1}{3}$ *area of base × height*, find the volume of the pyramid, rounded to the nearest tenth.

_____

20. Using the formula *volume of cylinder* = $\pi r^2 h$, find the volume of the cylinder, rounded to the nearest tenth. Use 3.14 for π.

_____

Use the coordinate plane to solve problems 21–25.

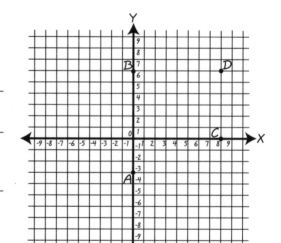

21. Find the distance between points A and B.

_____

22. Find the coordinates of point D.

_____

23. Find the distance between points B and D.

_____

24. Find the slope of a line passing through points B and C, using the formula:

$$\frac{\text{change in } y\text{-units}}{\text{change in } x\text{-units}}$$

_____

25. Use the Pythagorean theorem $a^2 + b^2 = c^2$ to find the hypotenuse (c) of the triangle formed by points B, C, and D.

_____

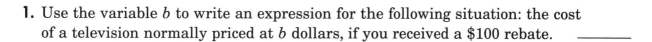

FORMULAS

1. Use the variable b to write an expression for the following situation: the cost of a television normally priced at b dollars, if you received a $100 rebate. _____

2. Simplify the expression. $4z - 2z \div 2$ _____

3. Find the value of the expression for the given variable.

   $2r + 6r \div 4; r = 2$ _____

4. Solve for a. $\frac{a - 15}{4} = 9$ _____

5. Solve for a. $a(b + c) = d$ _____

Use the formulas provided to solve problems 6–10.

6. $d = rt$; solve for r when $d = 220$ mi and $t = 5.5$ hr _____

7. $C = \frac{5}{9}(F - 32)$; solve for C when F = 64. Round to the nearest degree. _____

8. $i = prt$; solve for p when $r = 6.8\%$, $t = 2$ years, and $i = \$163.20$ _____

9. sales tax = rate × price; total cost = price + sales tax; solve for total cost when price = $189 and rate = 7% _____

10. discount = rate × original price; final cost = original price − discount. Find the total cost when original price = $531 and rate of discount = 15%. _____

11. Find the perimeter of the rectangle using the formula:
    $perimeter = 2 \times length + 2 \times width$. _____

12. Find the area of the rectangle using the formula: $area = length \times width$. _____

13. Find the circumference of the circle using the formula: $circumference = 2\pi r$, where $\pi = \frac{22}{7}$ and $r = $ radius. _____

14. Find the area of the circle using the formula: $area = \pi r^2$, where $\pi = 3.14$ and $r = $ radius. Round to the nearest tenth. _____

15. Find the area of a parallelogram with a height of 7.3 in. and a base of 6.1 in. The formula is: *area = base × height*. _____

16. Find the area of a triangle with a base of $5\frac{1}{2}$ cm and a height of $3\frac{1}{8}$ cm. The formula is: $area = \frac{1}{2} \ base \times height$. _____

Use the figures to solve problems 17–20.

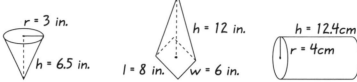

17. Using the formula *volume of prism = lwh*, find the volume of the prism, rounded to the nearest tenth. _____

18. Using the formula $volume \ of \ cone = \frac{1}{3}\pi r^2 h$, find the volume of the cone, rounded to the nearest tenth. Use 3.14 for π. _____

19. Using the formula $volume \ of \ pyramid = \frac{1}{3} \ area \ of \ base \times height$, find the volume of the pyramid, rounded to the nearest tenth. _____

20. Using the formula $volume \ of \ cylinder = \pi r^2 h$, find the volume of the cylinder, rounded to the nearest tenth. Use 3.14 for π. _____

Use the coordinate plane to solve problems 21–25.

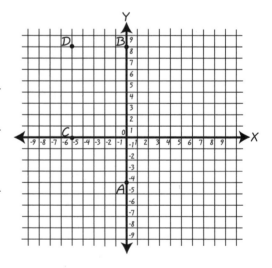

21. Find the distance between points A and B. _____

22. Find the coordinates of point D. _____

23. Find the distance between points B and D. _____

24. Find the slope of a line passing through points B and C, using the formula:

change in *y*-units
―――――――――
change in *x*-units _____

25. Use the Pythagorean theorem $a^2 + b^2 = c^2$ to find the hypotenuse (*c*) of the triangle formed by points A, B, and D. _____

1. Write the following as a base with an exponent. $3 \times 3 \times 3 \times 3$ _____

2. Find the value of 4^5. _____

Simplify problems 3–5.

3. $(6 + 2) \times 2^4$ _____   4. $(24 - 17)^2 - (2 + 1)^3$ _____   5. $(1.5)^3 + (0.3)^2$ _____

Use the figure to solve problems 6 and 7.

6. Find the area of the circle using the formula $A = \pi r^2$ where r = radius.

   Use 3.14 for π. _____

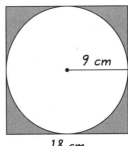

9 cm

18 cm

7. The formula for the area of a square is $A = s^2$, where s = side.

   Find the area of the shaded region in the figure. _____

8. Find the volume of a cube with $s = 3$ in. using the formula

   $V = s^3$ where s = side. _____

Simplify problems 9 and 10. Write the answer in exponents.

9. $5^3 \times 5^4$ _____   10. $\dfrac{16^5}{16^3}$ _____

Simplify the expressions in problems 11–13.

11. $\dfrac{8^4}{2^4} - (1^2)^5 + (6 - 1)^2$ _____   12. $5^{-5} \div 5^{-3}$ _____   13. $6^2 \times 6^{-4} + \dfrac{5^{-4}}{5^{-5}}$ _____

14. Write the number 420,000 in scientific notation. _____

15. Write the number 2.3×10^{-4} in standard notation. _____

Simplify problems 16–17. Write the answer in scientific notation.

16. $\dfrac{(7 \times 10^4)}{(3.1)} \times (10^2)$ _____   17. $(1.5 \times 10^{-3}) \times (6.2 \times 10^4)$ _____

18. Alpha Centauri is the nearest star to Earth, other than the Sun. It is 4.3 light-years away. 1 light-year equals 5.88×10^{12} km. Write the distance from Alpha Centauri in km using scientific notation. _____

19. Jupiter is 4.83×10^8 mi from the Sun. Earth is 9.32×10^6 mi from the Sun. How many times as far is the distance from Jupiter to the sun as the distance from the sun to the Earth? Round to the nearest whole number. _____

20. Light travels at a speed of 1.86×10^5 miles per second. Find how far light will travel in 3 minutes. _____

21. The nucleus of an atom of helium has 2 protons and 2 neutrons. The mass of 1 proton or 1 neutron is about 1.7×10^{-24} g. Find the mass of the helium nucleus. _____

22. In 1993 the national debt of the United States was 4,351.2 billion dollars. Write the national debt using scientific notation. _____

23. Arturo borrowed $1,000 from the bank at an 8% interest rate, compounded quarterly. Find the amount of interest Arturo will pay if he pays off the loan in 1 year. _____

24. The population of Brazil was 159,739,000 in 1994. The growth rate was 1.3% per year. Assuming the growth rate continues at the same percent, find the population of Brazil in 1997. Round to the nearest whole number. _____

Use the mortgage payment table to solve problem 25.

Amount financed	10 years	15 years	20 years	25 years	30 years
$25,000	303.32	238.91	209.11	192.95	183.44
$35,000	424.65	334.48	292.75	270.14	256.82

25. Sally and Frank took out a $35,000 mortgage to be paid back monthly over 15 years. The above table shows the monthly payments they must make at an 8% annual interest. Find the amount of interest Sally and Frank will have paid the bank after 15 years. _____

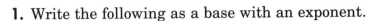

EXPONENTS AND SCIENTIFIC NOTATION

1. Write the following as a base with an exponent.

$4 \times 4 \times 4 \times 4 \times 4$ _____

2. Find the value of 9^3. _____

Simplify problems 3–5.

3. $(68 - 4) \div 4^2$ _____ **4.** $10^2 - (3 \times 2)^2 - 18$ _____ **5.** $(\frac{2}{3})^3$ _____

Use the figure to solve problems 6 and 7.

6. The formula for the area of a square is $A = s^2$ where s = side. Find the area of the circle using the formula $A = \pi r^2$ where r = radius. Use 3.14 for π.

_____

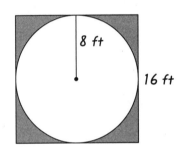

7. Find the area of the shaded region in the figure.

_____

8. Find the volume of a cylinder with $r = 3$ cm and $h = 5$ cm using the formula $V = \pi r^2 h$ where r = radius and h = height. Use 3.14 for π. _____

Simplify problems 9 and 10. Write the answer in exponents.

9. $(7^2)^3$ _____ **10.** $\frac{12^6}{2^6}$ _____

Simplify the expressions in problems 11–13.

11. $\frac{4^4}{4^2} + (2^2)^3 - (2 + 5)^2$ _____ **12.** $4^{-4} \div 4^{-2}$ _____ **13.** $3^2 \times 3^{-2} + \frac{2^{-2}}{2^{-3}}$ _____

14. Write the number 0.000065 in scientific notation. _____

15. Write the number 8.5×10^6 in standard notation. _____

Simplify problems 16 and 17. Write the answer in scientific notation.

16. $(4.7 \times 10^3) \times (6.2 \times 10^2)$ _____ **17.** $(5.4 \times 10^{-4}) \times (8 \times 10^2)$ _____

Use the table to solve problems 18–20.

18. Find how much farther Mars is from the Sun than Earth is from the Sun. _____

19. How many times as far is the distance from Jupiter to the Sun as the distance from Mercury to the Sun?

    Round to the nearest tenth. _____

Average Distance from Selected Planets to Sun

Planet	Distance in mi
Mercury	3.6×10^7
Venus	6.71×10^7
Earth	9.32×10^7
Mars	1.42×10^8
Jupiter	4.83×10^8

20. The speed of light is 1.86×10^5 miles per second. Find how many seconds it takes for light from the Sun to reach Earth. Round to the nearest second. _____

21. The nucleus of an atom of carbon-14 has 6 protons and 8 neutrons. The mass of 1 proton or 1 neutron is about 1.7×10^{-24} g. Find the mass of the carbon-14 nucleus. _____

22. In 1991 the national debt of the United States was 3,665.3 billion dollars. Write the national debt using scientific notation. _____

23. Miguel borrowed $1,200 from the bank at an interest rate of 12%, compounded semi-annually. Find the amount of interest Miguel will have to pay if he pays off the loan in 2 years. _____

24. The population of Egypt was 59,325,000 in 1994. The annual growth rate was 2.3%. Assuming the growth rate continues at the same percent, find the population of Egypt in 1998. Round to the nearest whole number. _____

Use the mortgage payment table to solve problem 25.

Amount financed	10 years	15 years	20 years	25 years	30 years
$25,000	303.32	238.91	209.11	192.95	183.44
$35,000	424.65	334.48	292.75	270.14	256.82

25. Theresa and John took out a $25,000 mortgage to be paid back monthly over 25 years. The above table shows the monthly payments they must make at an 8% annual interest. Find the amount of interest Theresa and John will have paid the bank after 25 years. _____

PROBLEM SOLVING STRATEGIES

1. A tape player costs $53.96 at House of Sounds and $62.49 at Max-Music. Tapes at Max-Music cost $8.99. How much less does a tape player cost at House of Sounds than at Max-Music? _____

Use the ad to solve problems 2–5.

> *Whiz Cereal:* **$2.49** a box   *Coffee:* **2 cans for $7.00**
> *Yellow corn:* **4 ears for $1.00**   *Blueberries:* **$1.98** a box

2. Graciela buys a box of cereal and a box of berries. How much change does she get from a $5 bill? _____

3. Tell what steps you used to solve the problem.

_____

4. Give another method of solving the problem.

_____

_____

5. Write a problem that can be solved using information given in the ad. Then solve the problem.

Problem: _____

_____

Solution: _____

6. List the coin combination (quarters, dimes, nickels, and/or pennies) that will make $0.74 using the fewest coins.

_____

7. Raquel has 100 feet of fencing. What is the area of the largest 4-sided figure Raquel can enclose in a 100-foot perimeter?

_____

8. Lupe has a 10 A.M. appointment. It will take her 45 minutes to get dressed and 30 minutes to drive there. When must Lupe begin to get dressed so she can arrive on time? _____

9. Find the sum of all whole numbers from 1 to 24.

_____

10. You have 4 bills—a $20, a $10, a $5, and a $1. List all of the *amounts* (not just the combinations) that can be made by combining only 2 bills at a time.

_____

11. Find the area of the figure shown in the diagram at the right.
Use the formula $A = lw$.   Area: _____

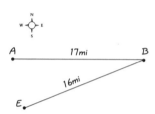

Complete the diagram to solve.

12. The diagram already shows Roads AB and BE. Road BC runs from north to south and is 14 miles long. Road CD runs from east to west and is 15 miles long. Road DE runs north and is 4 miles long. Road EA connects points E and A and is 7 miles long. What is the shortest route from point A to point C?

_____

13. In Week 1, Alia has 6 drawings and 10 paintings that she made to sell. Suppose she makes 4 new drawings and 2 new paintings each week. At what week will she have more drawings than paintings?   _____

14. Roger makes the following pattern of dots in each row of an abstract painting:

Row 1: 12 dots   Row 2: 24 dots   Row 3: 20 dots   Row 4: 40 dots   Row 5: 36 dots

How many dots will be in the ninth row? (Hint: make a table to help you.)   _____

15. In a survey, 80 people were asked if they liked broccoli or cauliflower. 45 said they liked broccoli, and 52 said they liked cauliflower. Of these, 18 liked both vegetables. How many liked cauliflower but not broccoli? (Hint: draw a Venn diagram.)   _____

16. Four friends each have a different favorite color.
   Friends: Kay, Jim, Ana, Tom   Colors: red, orange, blue, gold
   - Neither of the boys has orange as a favorite color.
   - Kay loves Valentine's day because it celebrates her color.
   - Jim saw Tom buy a blue vest and blue boots.

Who has which favorite color?   _____

1. Dennis earned $564 last week. He worked 40 hours that week. Next week he plans to work 8 hours in overtime. How much money did Dennis earn per hour last week? _____

Use the ad to solve problems 2–5.

Apples: **$.89** a pound   *Carrots:* 2 bunches **$1.18**
Paper towels: 3 rolls **$1.20**   *Cat food:* 3 cans **$1.59**

2. Andy wants to buy only 2 cans of cat food. How much will they cost? (Don't worry about including sales tax.) _____

3. Tell what steps you used to solve the problem. _____

4. Give another method of solving the problem.

_____

_____

5. Write a problem that can be solved using information given in the ad. Then solve the problem.

Problem: _____

_____

Solution: _____

6. List the coin combination (quarters, dimes, nickels, and/or pennies) that will make $0.83 using the fewest coins.

_____

7. Anton has enough 12-inch square tiles to cover 52 square feet of floor. What is the largest perimeter he can cover with the tiles?

_____

8. A suit cost a customer $132.57. Of that price, sales tax was $12.57. The salesperson's commission was $15.25. The store's profit was $38.35. How much did the store originally pay for the suit when it was bought wholesale? _____

9. Find the sum of all whole numbers from 1 to 34.

_____

10. You have 1 quarter, 1 dime, 1 nickel, and 1 penny. List all *amounts* (not just the combinations) that can be made by combining only 2 coins at a time.

_____

11. Find the area of the figure shown in the diagram.
Use the formula $A = lw$ Area: _____

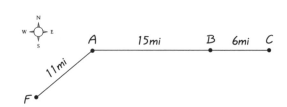

Complete the diagram to solve.

12. The diagram already shows Roads ABC and AF. Road AE runs south and is 14 miles long. Road CD runs south and is 15 miles long. Road DE is 20 miles long. Road EF is 12 miles long. What is the *longest* route from point B to point F?

_____

13. One job pays $9 an hour and offers a raise of $0.75 every 6 months. Another job pays $10 an hour and offers a raise of $0.50 every 6 months. How many months will it take before the jobs pay the same amount?   _____

14. A radio program gives out prizes every hour in this pattern:

Hour 1: 6 prizes   Hour 2: 12 prizes   Hour 3: 9 prizes
Hour 4: 15 prizes   Hour 5: 12 prizes   Hour 6: 18 prizes

How many prizes will be given out in the 10th hour?
(Hint: make a table to help you.)   _____

15. Of the 14 hockey teams in the league, 12 played on Saturday, and 8 played on Sunday. Of these teams, 6 played both Saturday and Sunday. How many teams played only on Saturday? (Hint: draw a Venn diagram.)   _____

16. George, Lily, Ella, and Dan are brothers and sisters. One is a doctor. One is a lawyer. One owns a bakery. One is a teacher.

- **The teacher is not a woman.**
- **Ella's sister recently took care of Ella's sprained wrist.**
- **Dan and Ella love shopping at their relative's bakery.**

Who does which job? _____

ONE- AND TWO-STEP PROBLEMS

1. For lunch, Charlotte had a sandwich for $3.75, fries for $0.74, a salad for $0.99, and iced tea for $0.81. The sales tax came to $0.38. How much change will she get from $10? _____

2. Li had a balance of $634.20 in his checking account. Then he wrote two checks—one for $113.67 and another for $49.23. Find Li's new balance. _____

3. This week, Mario has run $1\frac{3}{4}$ miles, $2\frac{1}{4}$ miles, and $3\frac{1}{2}$ miles. He wants to run 9 miles by the end of the week. How many more miles must he run? _____

4. Find the sales tax on a dinner costing $14.52 at a tax rate of 8%. Round to the nearest cent. _____

5. Find the cost of a food processor on sale for 15% off. The food processor normally sells for $73.99. Round to the nearest cent. _____

6. A car battery costs $49.56 after tax and $46.75 before tax. Find the tax rate percent. Round to the nearest percent. _____

7. Last week, 35% of the parts made in a factory were defective. There were 721 defective parts. Find how many parts were made. _____

8. Alejandro hears that the outdoor temperature is 15°C. If the temperature is below 60°F, he should wear a jacket. Should Alejandro wear a jacket today? (Hint: To convert the temperature to Fahrenheit, use the formula $F = \frac{9}{5}C + 32$.) _____

9. Charlene is making a muffin recipe that calls for 2 eggs for every 4 cups of flour. She has 14 eggs but only 16 cups of flour. If she makes enough muffins to use up all her flour, how many eggs will she have left? _____

Use the amounts below to solve problems 10–12.

$25 $20 $15 $40 $20 $10 $15 $15

10. Find the mean for the amounts. _____

11. Find the median for the amounts. _____

12. Find the mode for the amounts. _____

Complete the table. Use it to solve problems 13–14.

Education Levels of Adults in Wilton (Total adult population: 375,400)

Education	Number of People	Percent
4 years of high school	255,272	
1–3 years of college	45,048	
4 years or more of college	75,080	

13. What percent of the adult population of Wilton has completed 4 years or more of college? _____

14. What percent of the adult population has completed 1–4 years of college or more? _____

Use the graph to solve problems 15–17.

15. Which town or towns have a population of 150,000 or more?

_____

16. How much greater is the population of Olympus than the population of Shawnee?

_____

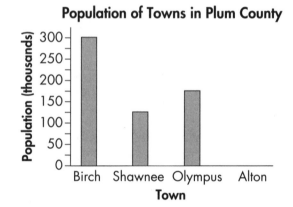

Population of Towns in Plum County

17. The city of Alton has a population of 225,000. Add a bar showing this data to the graph.

18. A rectangle is 15 ft on its longer side. The shorter side is $\frac{2}{3}$ the length of the longer side. Find the area of the rectangle. _____

19. Find the probability of choosing a number divisible by 3 from slips of paper containing the numbers 1 through 10. _____

20. One morning the temperature was 6°. Then it fell 3°, rose 2°, and fell 7°. What was the temperature then? _____

1. Dean buys 2 tires for $29.27 each. The sales tax comes to $2.53. He gives the cashier $70. How much change will he get back? _____

2. Ricardo had a balance of $591.03 in his checking account. He wrote a check for $288.47 and made a deposit of $120.53. Find Ricardo's new balance. _____

3. Mr. Thaler had 20 yd of ribbon. He made 3 sales: $4\frac{1}{4}$ yd, $7\frac{1}{2}$ yd, and $3\frac{3}{4}$ yd. How much of the ribbon is left? _____

4. Find the discount on a sofa normally selling at $654 but that is now 25% off. Round to the nearest cent. _____

5. Mrs. Yokoi buys a lawnmower costing $159.99. She must pay 6% sales tax. Find the total cost. Round to the nearest cent. _____

6. A gold chain costs $128.94 after tax and $120.50 before tax. Find the tax rate percent. Round to the nearest percent. _____

7. A road crew fixed 36 potholes. This was 48% of the potholes in city streets. How many potholes were there before repairs? _____

8. Lisa hears that the outdoor temperature is 78°F. Then she learns by shortwave radio that the temperature in Madrid, Spain, is 24°C. Is the temperature warmer in Madrid or in Lisa's town? (Hint: To convert the Celsius temperature to Fahrenheit, use the formula $F = \frac{9}{5}C + 32$.) _____

9. Phil uses 12 gallons of gasoline driving to work for 5 days. How much gasoline would Phil use in 25 days? _____

Use the amounts below to solve problems 10–12.

   8   9   10   2   1   8   2   8

10. Find the mean for the amounts. _____

11. Find the median for the amounts. _____

12. Find the mode for the amounts. _____

Complete the table. Use it to solve problems 13–14.

Mayoral Election Results for Ojibway City (Total number of ballots cast: 364,700)

Candidate	Number of Votes	Percent
Jackson Vega	164,115	
Priscilla Scott	109,410	
Todd Kawahara	91,175	

13. If no candidate received 50% of the votes, there must be a runoff election. Must there be a runoff? _____

14. Suppose that half of the people who voted for Scott had voted for Kawahara instead. How many votes would Kawahara have received? _____

Use the graph to solve problems 15–17.

15. Which magazine or magazines sold over 100,000 copies?

_____

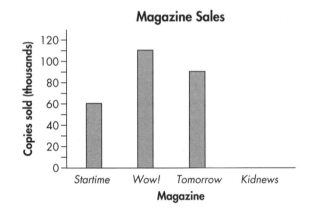

16. *Startime* and *Tomorrow* are both published by the same company. What is the combined sales of these two magazines?

_____

17. A new magazine, *Kidnews,* sold 30,000 copies of its first issue. Add a bar showing this data to the graph.

18. A rectangle is 6 ft on one side. Its area is 24 sq. ft. What is its perimeter? _____

19. A bag contains 3 blue marbles, 6 red marbles, 5 clear marbles, and 4 green marbles. What is the probability of reaching into the bag and picking out a red marble? _____

20. On his diet, Dennis lost 5 lb the first week, gained 2 lb the second week, and lost 4 lb the third week. If his wife promised him $2.50 for each pound he lost, how much does she owe Dennis after the the third week? _____

1. List the next three numbers in this pattern of multiples. Then find the 15th multiple.

6, 12, 18, _____, _____, _____   15th multiple: _____

2. The following pattern follows the rule $4n - 3$. Enter the next two terms (numbers). Then find the 20th term.

1, 5, 9, _____, _____   20th term: _____

3. The first four terms are given. Write the rule. Then write the 15th term.

8, 11, 14, 17   Rule: _____   15th term: _____

4. Draw the figure that follows in the sequence shown below.

5. Find the next-highest prime number after 43. _____

6. Write the prime factorization of 20. _____

7. Write at least one pair of prime numbers whose sum is 18. (Hint: 1 is *not* a prime number.)   _____

8. Write at least one set of three prime numbers whose sum is 35.   _____

9. Find the next number in this pattern.   6, 36, 216, _____

10. Find the next number in this pattern.   4096, 512, 64, _____

11. Write the next three numbers in the sequence. Then state or describe the rule.

3, 14, 10, 21, 17, _____, _____, _____

Rule: _____

12. Five friends took a long-distance, around-the-clock car trip. Each person took a turn driving the car for 3 hours. Mimi finished her turn at 6 P.M. Find the time that Mimi must begin her next turn driving. _____

13. February 14, 1995, fell on a Tuesday. Find the day that February 14, 1999, will fall on. (Hint: 1996 is a leap year.) _____

Use the function rule to complete the table, find ordered pairs, and graph the linear function.

14. Rule: $y = 3x - 1$

x	3x-1
-2	____
0	____
1	____
2	____
3	____

15. Write the ordered pairs.

←(____ , ____)

←(____ , ____)

←(____ , ____)

←(____ , ____)

←(____ , ____)

16. Plot the points on the grid.

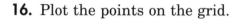
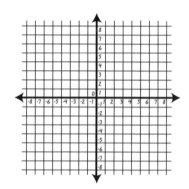

17. Look at triangle ABC on the grid. Suppose you slide the triangle 2 units to the right on the *x* axis. Then you rotate it 180° clockwise around vertex A. Where will vertex B end up? Give the new coordinates. (Hint: Use tracing paper to help you.)

_____

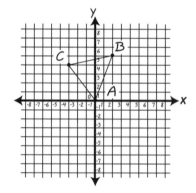

Use the figures to solve problems 18 and 19.

18. The triangle is an isosceles triangle. If ∠ A is increased by 10°, find the angles of ∠ B and ∠ C that would keep the figure an isosceles triangle. _____

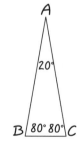
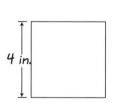

19. If the side of the square is doubled, by what factor does the area increase? _____

20. The two legs of a Pythagorean triangle are 24 and 45. Find the hypoteneuse. _____

PATTERNS AND FUNCTIONS

1. List the next three numbers in this pattern of multiples. Then find the 18th multiple.

    4, 8, 12, _____, _____, _____   18th multiple: _____

2. The following pattern follows the rule $5n - 2$. Enter the next two terms (numbers). Then find the 21st term.

    3, 8, 13, _____, _____   21st term: _____

3. The first four terms are given. Write the rule. Then write the 19th term.

    4, 11, 18, 25, _____   Rule: _____   19th term: _____

4. Draw the figure that follows in the sequence shown below.

5. Find the next-highest prime number after 31. _____

6. Write the prime factorization of 18. _____

7. Write at least one pair of prime numbers whose sum is 24.
    (Hint: 1 is *not* a prime number.)   _____

8. Write at least one set of three prime numbers whose sum is 15.   _____

9. Find the next number in this pattern.   4, 16, 64, _____

10. Find the next number in this pattern.   625, 125, 25, _____

11. Write the next three numbers in the sequence. Then state or describe the rule.

    1, 4, 5, 9, 14, 23, _____, _____, _____

    Rule: _____

12. This week Mia must take medication every 5 hours around the clock. If she takes her first dose at 10 A.M., when will she take her sixth dose?   _____

13. Monday, April 10, 1995, was Eduardo's 18th birthday. Give the day of the week and the year of his 21st birthday. (Hint: 1996 is a leap year.) _____

Use the function rule to complete the table, find ordered pairs, and graph the linear function.

14. Rule: $y = 2x + 1$ **15.** Write the ordered pairs.   **16.** Plot the points on the grid.

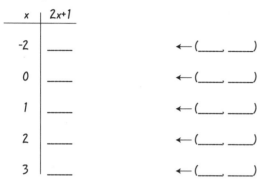

x	2x+1
-2	____
0	____
1	____
2	____
3	____

←(____, ____)

←(____, ____)

←(____, ____)

←(____, ____)

←(____, ____)

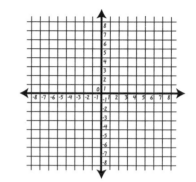

17. Look at triangle ABC on the grid. Suppose you slide the triangle down 3 units on the y axis. Then you rotate it 180° clockwise around vertex A. Where will vertex B end up? Give the new coordinates. (Hint: Use tracing paper to help you.)

_____

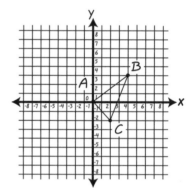

Use the figures to solve problems 18 and 19.

18. The triangle is an isosceles triangle. If ∠ A is decreased by 10°, find the angles of ∠ B and ∠ C that would keep the figure an isosceles triangle. _____

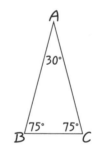

19. If the radius of the circle is doubled, by what factor does the area increase? _____

20. The two legs of a Pythagorean triangle are 30 and 72. Find the hypoteneuse. _____

LOCATOR TEST

1. 1,032
2. 2,609
3. 169,993
4. 532
5. 1 7/12
6. 2 13/20
7. 3 2/3
8. 4/25
9. 16 rebounds
10. 8 defective parts
11. 24 ft
12. 48 ft
13. 6.857
14. 48.52
15. 902.851
16. 125.4
17. 292
18. 867
19. $129.84
20. $120.75
21. 96
22. .523
23. 19.5 m
24. 200.96 in.^{2}
25. 32
26. 8 above, 24 below
27. $372
28. 196 ft^2
29. 8 employees
30. 2:40 P.M.
31. 40 ft
32. $342.88
33. 1/2 or 3/6
34. 600
35. 18
36. 350 ft^2
37. 5.125%
38. 5%
39. 4%
40. 1/8
41. 8/15
42. 5/34
43. $n = 8$
44. 376.8 cm^3
45. (2, 11)
46. 5×7
47. Wednesday
48. 5.86×10^9
49. 640,000,000
50. 88

Items	Book
1–4	Whole Numbers & Integers
5–8	Fractions
9–12	Ratios & Proportions
13–16	Decimals
17–20	Percents
21–24	Measurement & Geometry
25–27	Graphing & Interpreting Data
28–30	Problem-Solving Strategies
31–33	One-and Two-Step Problems
34–36	Estimation
37–39	Basic Statistics
40–42	Probability
43–44	Formulas
45–47	Patterns and Functions
48–50	Exponents & Scientific Notation

WHOLE NUMBERS AND INTEGERS

TEST 1

1. 390
2. 800
3. 772
4. 228
5. 135,342
6. 243
7. 1,800
8. 11
9. $12
10. $17
11. <
12.

13. ⁻1
14. ⁻77
15. ⁻7
16. ⁺304
17. ⁻104
18. ⁺806
19. ⁻22
20. 39
21. 260
22. 18
23. 21
24. H
25. (⁻2,5)

TEST 2

1. 300
2. 700
3. 583
4. 64
5. 79,488
6. 80
7. 1,000
8. 6
9. $120
10. 8

11. >

12.

13. ⁻7
14. ⁻21
15. ⁺22
16. ⁻153
17. ⁻306
18. ⁻720
19. ⁻250
20. 110
21. ⁻3
22. $21
23. 31
24. A
25. (⁻4, ⁻3)

Review	
Items	**Lessons**
1	1–2
2	3
3	4
4	5
5	6–8
6	9
7	7
8	10
9	11–13
10	14
11	15
12	16
13	17
14	18
15	19
16	20
17	21–22

18	23
19	24
20–21	25
22	26
23	27
24–25	28

FRACTIONS

TEST 1

1. 2, 3, 5
2. 15
3. 4/7
4. 2/3
5. 3/12, 10/12
6. .75
7. 11/20
8. 3/8, 2/5, 2/3
9. 3 1/8
10. 17/3
11. 3 1/4
12. 13 1/2
13. 1 2/9
14. 1 5/12
15. 8 5/24
16. 1/2
17. 1/12
18. 2 3/16 in.
19. 2 3/4 cups
20. 8/15
21. 6 6/7
22. 1 3/5
23. 14 servings
24. 86%
25. 3/20

TEST 2

1. 5, 7
2. 30
3. 3/8
4. 3/4
5. 3/18, 8/18
6. .375
7. 7/8
8. 2/7, 1/3, 3/8
9. 4 1/3
10. 31/7
11. 5 1/5
12. 1/2
13. 1 4/7
14. 1 1/12
15. 9 7/24
16. 1/3
17. 2/15
18. 2 1/10 mi
19. 3 3/4 pounds
20. 1/2
21. 6
22. 1 7/9
23. 7 1/3
24. 21%
25. 11/25

Review	
Items	**Lessons**
1	1
2	2
3	3
4	4
5	5
6	6
7	7
8	8
9, 10	9

11	10
12	11
13	12
14	13
15	14
16	15
17	16
18	17
19	18
20	1
21	20
22	21
23	22
24	23
25	24, 25

RATIOS AND PROPORTIONS

TEST 1

1. 3/7; 3:7
2. yes
3. 5/11
4. 3/8
5. <
6. 5/8, 13/20, 7/10
7. $9.26/hr
8. $0.74/lb
9. 48 walks
10. yes
11. no
12. 6
13. 480
14. $7.36
15. 19.56 ft/sec
16. 25 ft
17. 1 1/2 miles
18. 1
19. 6
20. 27 ft
21. no
22. 50.24 cm
23. 16π mm^2
24. 1/5; 1/25; 25
25. 42.875 in.^{3}

TEST 2

1. 6/5; 6:5
2. yes
3. 7/10
4. 9/20
5. <
6. 15/28, 4/7, 3/5
7. 30 mph
8. $1.35/gal
9. 13 home runs
10. no
11. yes
12. 15
13. 27 boards
14. $131.25
15. 352 ft/min
16. 18 ft
17. 18 miles
18. 2
19. 6
20. 44 ft
21. no
22. 43.96 cm
23. 25π in.^{2}
24. 10/60; 100/3600; 3600
25. 13.824 ft^3

REVIEW	
Items	Lessons
1	1
2	2
3	3
4	4
5, 6	5
7–8	6
9	7
10–11	8
12–13	9
14–15	10
16	11
17	12
18–19	13
20	14
21	15
22	16
23	17
24	18
25	19

DECIMALS

TEST 1

1. 6 thousandths
2. 6 hundredths
3. <
4. >
5. 812.30
6. 1.91
7. 64 3/8
8. 5.556
9. 13 m, 12.7 m
10. $19.52

11. 3.237 kilograms
12. 27.71
13. 3.347 km
14. $276.55
15. 54.7
16. 2.87154
17. $280, $284.62
18. 30.9603 m²
19. 1.4574
20. 51.87
21. $1.00, $.89
22. 24
23. 180%
24. 0.103
25. $3.44

TEST 2

1. 3 hundredths
2. 3 tenths
3. >
4. <
5. 34.10
6. 0.81
7. 21 1/8
8. 7.429
9. 34 km, 34.44 km
10. $66.39
11. 13.9 kilometers
12. 9.291
13. 881 grams or
    .881 kilograms
14. $13.87
15. 619
16. 80.8311
17. $400, $375.75
18. 25.387 m²
19. .39392
20. 62.54
21. $.60 or $.65, $.69
22. 16
23. 41.9%
24. 0.085
25. $19.37

Review	
Items	Lessons
1–2	1–2
3–4	3–4
5–7	5–7
8	7
9–11	8–10
12–14	11–12
15–18	13–16
19–22	17–20
23–25	21–22

PERCENTS

TEST 1

1. Shade 40 of 100
   squares
2. 0.39
3. 92%
4. 180%
5. 1/8
6. 22.75
7. 11.52
8. 6.25%
9. 25%
10. 300
11. 60
12. $13.56
13. $55.04
14. $1.16
15. $83.72
16. $43.02
17. $436
18. $51.25
19. estimate: accept from
    30%–40%;
    actual: 37.1%
20. 8%

21. 7%
22. 18%
23. 15%
24. 140
25. $14.36

TEST 2

1. Shade 15 of 100
   squares
2. 0.167
3. 40%
4. 112.5%
5. 1 3/5
6. 30.72
7. 19.68
8. 2.5%
9. 20%
10. 68.75
11. 81.25
12. $20.40
13. $16.39
14. $23.16
15. $19.52
16. $23.90
17. $450.60
18. $95.51
19. estimate: accept from
    .5%–1%;
    actual: 0.9%
20. 17%
21. 6%
22. 21%
23. 24%
24. 625
25. $201.04

REVIEW	
Items	Lessons
1	1
2–5	2–5, 11
6–7	6–7

8–9	11, 13, 14
10–11	11, 19, 20
12–13	8
14–15	9
16–17	10, 11
18	21
19	12, 13, 14
20	15
21	16
22–23	17
24	19,20
25	18, 22

MEASUREMENT AND GEOMETRY

TEST 1

1. 11 yd
2. 54 in.
3. 3 gal
4. 20 oz
5. 56 oz
6. 2.5 T
7. 82 cm
8. 12.69 L
9. 1,430 g
10. 95°
11. 55°
12. 56°
13. 180°
14. 2.5 m
15. 13 in.
16. 68 ft
17. 285 ft^2
18. 107.25 ft^2
19. 108 ft^2
20. 75.36 ft

21. 452.16 ft^2
22. Scalene
23. 35 square units
24. ($^-$7, 5)
25 C ($^-$3, 0) B (4, 0)
   F ($^-$3, $^-$5) D (4, $^-$5)

TEST 2

1. 18 in.
2. 9 yd
3. 1.5 gal
4. 24 oz
5. 40 oz
6. 1.5 T
7. 432 cm
8. 1.746 L
9. 6,700 g
10. 45°
11. 21°
12. 57°
13. 180°
14. 1 m
15. 25 cm
16. 10.5 m
17. 6.25 m^2
18. 9 m^2
19. 12 m^2
20. 21.98 m
21. 38.465 m^2
22. Scalene
23. 12 square units
24. (3, $^-$3)
25. A (5, 0) B ($^-$3, 0)
   C (0, 3) E ($^-$8, 3)

REVIEW	
Items	Lessons
1	1
2	1
3	3
4	3

5	4
6	4
7	5
8	7
9	8
10	11, 13
11	11, 13
12	18 19
13	18, 19
14	15
15	16
16	20
17	21
18	22
19	23
20	24
21	25
22	27, 28
23	29
24	30
25	30

ESTIMATION

TEST 1

Accept reasonable estimates based on different rounded numbers.

1. exact amount
2. 5,000; 4,200; 22,000
3. 91
4. $4.00
5. 1,300,000

6. about 26 days
7. 43.909
8. $16.00
9. 115
10. 4
11. 4,000; 330; 435
12. $750; overestimated
13. 8
14. 176
15. 20
16. 2
17. 25 1/2
18. 11
19. 20; 9
20. 24; 21 7/8
21. 36 km^2
22. 25%
23. 48 pages
24. 83%, 50%, 25%
25. $6.00

TEST 2

Accept reasonable estimates based on different rounded numbers.

1. estimate
2. 14,700; 3,000; 8,000
3. 89
4. 1,100 mi
5. 23,000,000
6. about 29 points
7. 13.8
8. $11.00
9. 108
10. 2
11. 200, 240, 248
12. $300; underestimated
13. 8
14. 72
15. 40
16. 1 1/2
17. 18 1/2

18. 5
19. 20, 8
20. 64, 68 1/16
21. 18 m^2
22. 75%
23. 12
24. 35%, 25%
25. $4.00 (accept $3.00)

Review	
Items	**Lessons**
1	1
2	2
3	3
4, 5	4, 5
6	6
7,8	7,8
9	9
10	10
11, 12	11, 12
13	13
14	14
15	15
16, 17	16, 17
18	18
19–21	19–21
22–24	22–24
25	25

GRAPHING AND INTERPRETING DATA

TEST 1

1. Hartford, CT
2. approximately $20,000
3. check students' graphs
4. 50,000
5. 5 picture symbols
6. 27%
7. 1/4
8. 32°
9. 10
10. 31.8
11. 30–34
12. 30–34
13. check students' graphs
14. 5
15. 3 hours
16. between 3 o'clock and 4 o'clock
17. (4, 2)
18. check students' grids:
   Point C: (3, 1);
   Point D: (⁻2, 3);
   Point E: (4, ⁻2)
19. (3, 9)
20. (3 + 3), (4 + 2), (5 + 1), (0 + 6), (1 + 5), (2 + 4), (6 + 0)

TEST 2

1. 3%
2. 1994
3. check students' graphs
4. 67.5 qBtu's
5. 1/2 symbol

6. 23%
7. 34.12 qBtu's
8. 14°
9. 5 students
10. 6.9
11. 7
12. 7
13. check students' graphs
14. 6 students
15. 3 hours
16. about 50
17. (3, 3)
18. check students' grids:
Point E: ($^-$3, $^-$2);
Point F: (4, 3);
Point G: (2, $^-$5)
19. (4, 10)
20. (0, 8), (1, 7), (2, 6), (3, 5), (4, 4), (5, 3), (6, 2), (7, 1), (8, 0)

REVIEW	
Items	Lessons
1	3 and 5
2	3 and 5
3	1, 4
4	6
5	7
6	11
7	11
8	12, 13
9	14
10	15
11	16
12	16
13	17
14	17

15	8, 24, 25
16	8, 24, 25
17	22
18	22
19	23
20	26

BASIC STATISTICS

TEST 1
1. 59.6, 58, 37, 47
2. 44
3. check students' graphs
4. 125 more
5. 1992
6. $1.75
7. 15
8. 0.333
9. $386.25
10. 36°
11. about $325
12. about $400
13. Students will probably conclude that earnings have steadily increased.
14. 52%
15. Average call is $19.50
16. about 7 or 8 women

TEST 2
1. 299.8, 305, 255, 385
2. 4.8%
3. check students' graphs
4. 20,000,000
5. Dallas/Ft. Worth and Los Angeles

6. R&B
7. 5
8. .250
9. 4,847
10. 108°
11. 1989
12. Answers will vary, but change will probably not be greater than 1.5%
13. Students will probably conclude that the percent of unemployment basically stays within a certain range.
14. 54%
15. serving size 1/6 of box
16. about 160 men

REVIEW	
Items	Lessons
1	1, 4, 7
2	1, 2, 3, 5
3	2, 3
4	8
5	8
6	9
7	9
8	11
9	12
10	12, 13
11	14
12	14, 15, 16, 21
13	14, 21
14	17
15	19
16	20

PROBABILITY

TEST 1

1. 6
2. 1/6, 1:6, 1 out of 6
3. 52
4. 1/52, 1:52, 1 out of 52
5. HHH, HHT, HTH,
THH, HTT, THT,
TTH, TTT
6. 3/8
7. 0
8. 24 out of 25
9. 3/5
10. 2/5
11. 1/10
12. 1,800,000
13. 3/4; likely
14. 5/8
15. 1/4
16. 1/8
17. 1/4
18. 9/16
19. 4/22
20. 1/552
21. 8/25
22. 17/25
23. 120
24. 24
25. 4

TEST 2

1. 8
2. 1/8
3. 100
4. 1/100
5. 1
6. 49/50
7. 1, 1; 1, 2; 1, 3; 1, 4; 2,
1; 2, 2; 2, 3; 2, 4; 3, 1;
3, 2; 3, 3; 3, 4; 4, 1; 4,
2; 4, 3; 4, 4
8. 1/4

9. 2/5
10. 2/5
11. 1/2
12. 1,000,000
13. 1/4; unlikely
14. 3/4
15. 1/3
16. 2/9
17. 1/16
18. 15/256
19. 1/17
20. 13/204
21. 4/7
22. 3/7
23. 720
24. 60
25. 6

REVIEW	
Items	**Lessons**
1–4	1–2
5–8	3–5
9–11	6, 7
12	8
13	9
14	10
15–16	11
17–18	12
19–20	13
21–22	14
23–24	15
25	16

FORMULAS

TEST 1

1. $\$.98y$
2. $5t/2$
3. 11
4. $a = 11.4$
5. $a = c/2b$
6. $t = 1.6$ hr
7. F = 82
8. $r = 6.2\%$
9. $21.64
10. $5.24
11. 14 cm
12. 12 cm^2
13. 37 5/7 in.
14. 113.0 in.^{2}
15. 11 7/8 cm^2
16. 13.44 in.^{2}
17. 22.6 in.^{3}
18. 167.5 cm^3
19. 1152 cm^3
20. 109.3 in.^{3}
21. 9
22. (8, 6)
23. 8
24. 3/4
25. 10

TEST 2

1. $b - \$100$
2. $3z$
3. 4
4. $a = 51$
5. $a = d/(b + c)$
6. $r = 40$ mph
7. C = 18
8. $p = \$1,200$
9. $202.23
10. $451.35
11. 20 cm
12. 25 cm^2
13. 31 3/7 in.

14. 78.5 in.^{2}
15. 44.53 in.^{2}
16. 8 19/32 cm^3
17. 243 cm^3
18. 61.2 in.^{3}
19. 192 in.^{3}
20. 623 cm^3
21. 12
22. ($^-$5, 8)
23. 5
24. 1 3/5
25. 13

REVIEW	
Items	**Lessons**
1	1
2–3	2–3
4–5	4–5
6	6
7	7
8	8
9	9
10	10
11–12	11, 13
13–14	12, 16
15	14
16	15
17–20	17–20
21	21
22–25	22–25

EXPONENTS AND SCIENTIFIC NOTATION

TEST 1

1. 3^4
2. 1,024
3. 128
4. 22
5. 3.465
6. 254.34 cm^2
7. 69.66 cm^2
8. 27 in.^{3}
9. 5^7
10. 16^2
11. 280
12. 1/25
13. 5 1/36
14. 4.2×10^5
15. 0.00023
16. 2.17×10^6
17. 9.3×10^1
18. 2.5284×10^{13} km
19. 52 times as far
20. 3.348×10^7 mi
21. 6.8×10^{-24} g
22. 4.3512×10^{12}
23. $82.43
24. 166,050,165
25. $25,206.40

TEST 2

1. 4^5
2. 729
3. 4
4. 46
5. 8/27
6. 200.96 ft^3
7. 55.04 ft^2
8. 141.3 cm^3
9. 7^6
10. 6^6
11. 31

12. 1/16
13. 3
14. 6.5×10^{-5}
15. 8,500,000
16. 2.914×10^6
17. 4.32×10^{-1}
18. 4.88×10^7 mi
19. 13 times as far
20. 501 seconds
21. 2.38×10^{-23} g
22. 3.6653×10^{12}
23. $314.97
24. 64,974,102
25. $57,885

Review	
Items	**Lessons**
1–2	1
3–5	2–4
6–8	5–7
9	8
10	9
11–13	10–12
14–15	13
16–17	14–15
18–20	16–17
21	18
22	19
23	20
24	21
25	22

PROBLEM SOLVING STRATEGIES

TEST 1

1. $8.53
2. $0.53
3. Possible answer: add $2.49 + $1.98; subtract the total ($4.47) from $5
4. Possible answer: subtract each number from $5
5. Problems should make logical use of the information given.
6. 2 quarters, 2 dimes, 4 pennies
7. 625 ft^2 (25 ft by 25 ft)
8. 8:45 A.M.
9. 300
10. $30, $25, $21, $15, $11, $6
11. 144 ft^2
12. AEDC (19 mi)
13. Week 4 (18 drawings, 16 paintings)
14. 132 dots
15. 34 people
16. Kay—red; Jim—gold; Ana—orange; Tom—blue

TEST 2

1. $14.10
2. $1.06
3. Possible answer: divide $1.59 ÷ 3, multiply $0.53 × 2
4. Possible answer: find 2/3 of $1.59
5. Problems should

make logical use of the information given.
6. 3 quarters, 1 nickel, 3 pennies
7. 106 ft (52 ft long, 1 ft wide)
8. $66.40
9. 595
10. $0.35, $0.30, $0.26, $0.15, $0.11, $0.06
11. 82 m^2
12. Accept BCDEF (53 mi) or BCDEAF (66 mi)
13. in 24 months ($12)
14. 24 prizes
15. 6 teams
16. George—baker; Lily—doctor; Ella—lawyer; Dan—teacher

REVIEW	
Items	Lessons
1	1, 3
2–4	1, 2, 17
5	4
6	5
7	6
8	8
9	16
10	13
11	9, 23
12	22
13	12
14	14, 15
15	19
16	20

ONE- AND TWO-STEP PROBLEMS

TEST 1

1. $3.33
2. $471.30
3. 1 1/2 miles
4. $1.16
5. $62.89
6. 6%
7. 2,060
8. yes (59°F)
9. 6 eggs
10. $20
11. $17.50
12. $15
13. 20%
14. 32%
15. Birch and Olympus
16. 50,000 greater
17. Check individual graphs.
18. 150 ft^2
19. 3/10
20. ⁻2°

TEST 2

1. $8.93
2. $423.09
3. 4 1/2 yd
4. $163.50
5. $169.59
6. 7%
7. 75 potholes
8. Lisa's town (Madrid is 75.2°F)
9. 60 gal
10. 6
11. 8
12. 8
13. yes (45% was the greatest amount)
14. 145,880 votes (40%)

15. *Wow!*
16. 150,000 copies
17. Check individual graphs.
18. 20 ft
19. 6/18 or 1/3
20. $17.50

REVIEW	
Items	Lessons
1	1, 2
2	3, 4
3	5, 6
4–7	7–12
8	13, 14
9	17, 18
10–12	27, 28
13–14	19, 20
15–17	20–24
18	25, 26
19	29, 30
20	31, 32

PATTERNS AND FUNCTIONS

TEST 1

1. 24, 30, 36; 15th multiple: 90
2. 13, 17; 20th term: 77
3. $3n + 5$; 15th term: 50
4. drawing of hexagon

5. 47
6. $2 \times 2 \times 5$
7. $5 + 13$ or $7 + 11$
8. Accept reasonable answers including $2 + 2 + 31$; $19 + 13 + 3$; or $23 + 7 + 5$
9. 1,296
10. 8
11. 28, 24, 35; add 11, then subtract 4
12. 6 A.M.
13. Sunday
14. $^-7$, $^-1$, 2, 5, 8
15. $(^-2,^-7)$, $(0,^-1)$, $(1,2)$, $(2,5)$, $(3,8)$
16. Check students' grids.
17. $(0,^-5)$
18. 75° each
19. 4
20. 51

TEST 2

1. 16, 20, 24; 18th multiple: 72
2. 18, 23; 21st term: 103
3. $7n - 3$; 19th term: 130
4. drawing of triangle
5. 37
6. $2 \times 3 \times 3$
7. $5 + 19$; $7 + 17$; or $11 + 13$
8. Accept reasonable answers including $2 + 2 + 11$; $3 + 7 + 5$; or $5 + 5 + 5$

9. 256
10. 5
11. 37, 60, 97; add the previous 2 terms
12. 11 A.M.
13. Friday, 1998
14. $^-3$, 1, 3, 5, 7
15. $(^-2,^-3)$, $(0,1)$, $(1,3)$, $(2,5)$, $(3,7)$
16. Check students' grids.
17. $(^-4,^-6)$
18. 80° each
19. 4
20. 78

REVIEW	
Items	Lessons
1–3	1–4
4	5
5–6	6, 7
7–8	23, 24
9–10	8
11	9
12–13	11, 12
14–16	3, 14, 16
17	7–19
18–19	20, 21
20	22